Table of Contents

PEARSON CUSTOM LIBRARY

G102
Intro to Earth Sci
Labratory Manual
Indiana University Northwest

PEARSON

Cover Art: Courtesy of Photodisc/Getty Images, Photoubrary.com, Robert Harding World Imagery, Getty Images/Photodisc.

Attention bookstores: For permission to return any unsold stock, contact us at *pe-uscustomreturns@pearson.com*.

Pearson Learning Solutions, 501 Boylston Street, Suite 900, Boston, MA 02116
A Pearson Education Company
www.pearsoned.com

Printed in the United States of America

30

ISBN 10: 1-256-20455-2
ISBN 13: 978-1-256-20455-8

The Study of Minerals

Objectives

Completion of this exercise will prepare you to:

A. Describe the physical properties commonly used to identify minerals.

B. Identify minerals using a mineral identification key.

C. Visually identify some common rock-forming minerals.

D. List the uses of several economic minerals.

Materials

mineral samples	dilute hydrochloric acid
streak plate	magnet
glass plate	hand lens

Introduction

For Earth science professionals and students learning about our planet, identifying minerals using relatively simple techniques is an important skill. Knowledge of common minerals and their properties is basic to an understanding of rocks. This exercise introduces the common physical and chemical properties of minerals and how these properties are used to identify minerals.

What Is a Mineral?

Geologists define a **mineral** as *any naturally occurring inorganic solid that possesses an orderly crystalline structure and can be represented by a chemical formula.* Thus, Earth materials that are classified as minerals exhibit all of the following characteristics:

- **Naturally occurring** Minerals form by natural, geologic processes. Synthetic materials, meaning those produced in a laboratory or by human intervention, are not considered minerals.

- **Solid substance** Only crystalline substances that are solid at temperatures encountered at Earth's surface are considered minerals.

- **Orderly crystalline structure** Minerals are crystalline substances, which means their atoms are arranged in an orderly, repetitive manner.

- **Generally inorganic** Inorganic crystalline solids, such as ordinary table salt (halite), that are found naturally in the ground are considered minerals, whereas organic compounds, are generally not. Sugar, a crystalline solid like salt that comes from sugarcane or sugar beets, is a common example of an organic compound that is not considered a mineral.

- **Can be represented by a chemical formula** The common mineral quartz, for example, has the formula SiO_2, which indicates that quartz consists of silicon (Si) and oxygen (O) atoms in a ratio of one-to-two. This proportion of silicon to oxygen is true for any sample of quartz, regardless of its origin. However, the compositions of some minerals vary *within specific, well-defined limits.*

1. Use the geologic definition of a mineral to determine which of the items listed in Figure 1 are minerals and which are not minerals. Check the appropriate box.

Yes	No	Mineral	Yes	No	Mineral
		Rock candy			Obsidian
		Quartz			Cubic zirconia
		Motor oil			Hydrogen
		Emerald			Rain water
		Vitamin D			Halite

Figure 1 Which of these items are minerals?

From Exercise 1 of *Applications and Investigations in Earth Science*, Seventh Edition, Edward J. Tarbuck, Frederick K. Lutgens, Kenneth G. Pinzke, Dennis Tasa.

Physical Properties of Minerals

Minerals have definite crystalline structures and chemical compositions that give them unique sets of physical and chemical properties shared by all specimens of that mineral, regardless of when or where they form. For example, if you compare two samples of the mineral quartz, they will be equally hard and equally dense, and they will break in the same manner. However, the physical properties of individual samples may vary within specific limits due to ionic substitutions, inclusions of foreign elements (impurities), and defects in the crystal structure.

Diagnostic properties are particularly useful in mineral identification. The mineral magnetite, for example will attract a magnet, while the mineral halite has a salty taste. Because so few minerals share these properties, magnetism and salty taste are considered diagnostic properties of magnetite and halite, respectively.

Optical Properties

Luster   The appearance of light reflected from the surface of a mineral is known as **luster**. Minerals that have the appearance of metals, regardless of color, are said to have a **metallic luster**. Some metallic minerals, such as native copper and galena, develop a dull coating or tarnish when exposed to the atmosphere. Because they are not as shiny as samples with freshly broken surfaces, these samples exhibit a *submetallic luster*.

Most minerals have a **nonmetallic luster** and are described as *vitreous* (*glassy*), *dull* or *earthy* (a dull appearance like soil), or *pearly* (such as a pearl or the inside of a clamshell). Still others exhibit lusters that are *silky* (like silk or satin cloth) or *greasy* (as though coated in oil).

2. Examine the luster of the minerals in Figure 2. Place the letter A, B, C, D, or E in the space provided that corresponds to the luster exhibited. Letters may be used more than once. **A.** Metallic luster, **B.** Nonmetallic luster—glassy, **C.** Nonmetallic luster—dull, **D.** Nonmetallic luster—silky, **E.** Nonmetallic luster—greasy.

3. Examine the mineral specimens provided by your instructor and separate them into two groups—metallic and nonmetallic.

Metallic: _____

Nonmetallic: _____

The Ability to Transmit Light   Minerals are able to transmit light to different degrees. A mineral is described as **opaque** when no light is transmitted; **translucent** when light, but not an image, is transmitted; and **transparent** when both light and an image are visible through the sample.

Quartz

Galena

Limonite

Gypsum (selenite)

Talc

Native copper

Figure 2   Photos illustrating various types of mineral luster.

Color   Although **color** is generally the most conspicuous characteristic of a mineral, it is infrequently considered a diagnostic property.

4. Based on the samples of fluorite and quartz in Figure 3, why isn't color a diagnostic property of these two minerals?

_____

Streak   The *color* of a mineral in powdered form, called **streak**, is often useful in identification. A mineral's streak is obtained by rubbing it across a *streak plate* (a piece of unglazed porcelain) and observing the color of the mark it leaves. Although the color of a particular mineral may vary from sample to sample, its streak is usually consistent in color.

Streak can also help distinguish between minerals with metallic luster and those with nonmetallic luster. Metallic minerals generally have a dense, dark streak

A. Fluorite

B. Quartz

Figure 3   Color variation exhibited by **A.** fluorite and **B.** quartz.

Color: brassy
Streak: dark gray

Figure 4 Streak test.

(Figure 4), whereas minerals with nonmetallic luster typically have a light-colored streak.

Not all minerals produce a streak when rubbed across a streak plate. For example, the mineral quartz is harder than a streak plate. Therefore, it produces no streak using this method.

5. Figure 5 shows two specimens of the mineral hematite and their corresponding streaks. For both samples, describe the color of the specimen and the streak.

	COLOR OF SPECIMEN	STREAK
Specimen A:	_____	_____
Specimen B:	_____	_____

6. Select three of the mineral specimens provided by your instructor. Do they exhibit a streak? If so, is the streak the same color as the mineral specimen?

Figure 5 Hematite, an ore of iron, is found in both nonmetallic and metallic forms.

Figure 6 Using streak to assist in describing luster.

	COLOR OF SPECIMEN	STREAK
Specimen A:	_____	_____
Specimen B:	_____	_____
Specimen C:	_____	_____

7. To some observers, the mineral shown in Figure 6 exhibits a metallic luster, while others describe its luster as nonmetallic. Based on the streak of this sample, how would you describe its luster?

Luster: _____

Crystal Shape, or Habit

Recall that all minerals are crystalline, and when they form in unrestricted environments, they develop **crystals** that exhibit geometric shapes. For example, well-developed quartz crystals are hexagonal with pyramid-shaped ends, and garnet crystals are 12-sided (Figure 7). In addition, some crystals tend to grow and form characteristic shapes or patterns called **crystal shape**, or **habit**. Commonly used terms to describe various crystal habits include *bladed* (flat, elongated strips), *fibrous* (hair-like), *tabular* (tablet shaped), *granular* (aggregates of small crystals), *blocky* (square), and *banded* (layered).

Although crystal shape, or habit, is a diagnostic property for some specimens, many of the mineral samples you will encounter consist of crystals that are too minute to be seen with the unaided eye or are intergrown such that their shapes are not obvious.

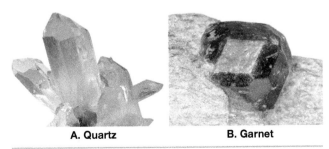

A. Quartz   **B. Garnet**

Figure 7 Characteristic crystal forms of **A.** quartz and **B.** garnet.

Specimen A   Specimen B

Specimen C   Specimen D

Figure 8 Crystal shapes and habits.

Figure 10 Sheets of elastic minerals, like muscovite, can be bent but will snap back when the stress is released.

8. Select one of the following terms to describe the crystal shape, or habit, of each specimen shown in Figure 8: cubic crystals, hexagonal crystals, fibrous habit, banded habit, blocky habit, bladed habit, tabular habit.

Specimen A: _____

Specimen B: _____

Specimen C: _____

Specimen D: _____

9. Use a *contact goniometer*, illustrated in Figure 9, to measure the angle between adjacent faces on the quartz crystals on display in the lab.

   a. Are the angles about the same for each quartz specimen, or do they vary from one sample to another? _____

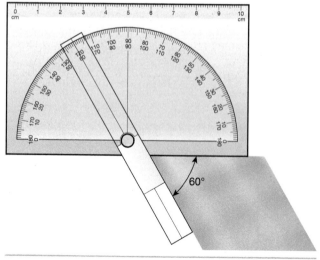

Figure 9 Contact goniometer.

   b. Write a generalization that describes how the angle between crystal faces relates to the shape of the sample. _____

Mineral Strength

How easily minerals break or deform under stress is determined by the type and strength of the chemical bonds that hold the crystals together.

Tenacity The term **tenacity** describes a mineral's resistance to breaking or deforming. Minerals that are ionically bonded, such as fluorite and halite, tend to be *brittle* and shatter into small pieces when struck. By contrast, minerals with metallic bonds, such as native copper, are *malleable*, or easily hammered into different shapes. Minerals, including gypsum and talc, that can be cut into thin shavings are described as *sectile*. Still others, notably the micas, are *elastic* and will bend and snap back to their original shape after the stress is released (Figure 10).

Hardness One of the most useful diagnostic properties is **hardness**, a measure of the resistance of a mineral to abrasion or scratching. This property is determined by rubbing a mineral of unknown hardness against one of known hardness or vice versa. A numerical value of hardness can be obtained by using the Mohs scale of hardness, which consists of 10 minerals arranged in order from 1 (softest) to 10 (hardest), as shown in Figure 11. It should be noted that the Mohs scale is a relative ranking; it does not imply that mineral number 2, gypsum, is twice as hard as mineral 1, talc.

10. The minerals shown in Figure 12 are fluorite and topaz that have been tested for hardness. Use the Mohs scale in Figure 11 to identify which is fluorite and which is topaz.

MINERAL NAME

Specimen A: _____

Specimen B: _____

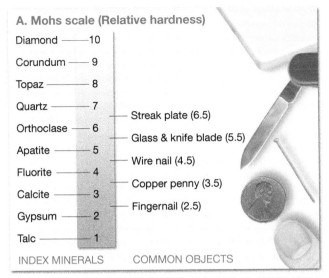

A. Mohs scale (Relative hardness)

INDEX MINERALS		COMMON OBJECTS
Diamond	10	
Corundum	9	
Topaz	8	
Quartz	7	
		Streak plate (6.5)
Orthoclase	6	
		Glass & knife blade (5.5)
Apatite	5	
		Wire nail (4.5)
Fluorite	4	
		Copper penny (3.5)
Calcite	3	
		Fingernail (2.5)
Gypsum	2	
Talc	1	

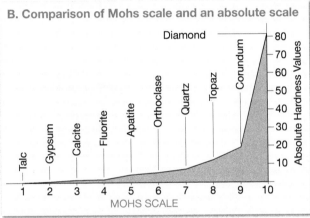

B. Comparison of Mohs scale and an absolute scale

Figure 11 Hardness scales. **A.** Mohs scale of hardness, with the hardness of some common objects. **B.** Relationship between the Mohs relative hardness scale and an absolute hardness scale.

In the laboratory, common objects are often used to determine the hardness of a mineral. These objects include a human fingernail, which has a hardness of about 2.5, a copper penny (3.5), and a piece of glass (5.5). The mineral gypsum, which has a hardness of 2,

Figure 12 Hardness test.

Table 1 Hardness Guide

HARDNESS	DESCRIPTION
Less than 2.5	A mineral that can be scratched by your fingernail (hardness = 2.5)
2.5 to 5.5	A mineral that cannot be scratched by your fingernail (hardness = 2.5) and cannot scratch glass (hardness = 5.5)
Greater than 5.5	A mineral that scratches glass (hardness = 5.5)

can be easily scratched with a fingernail. On the other hand, the mineral calcite, which has a hardness of 3, will scratch a fingernail but will not scratch glass. Quartz, one of the hardest common minerals, will easily scratch glass. Diamonds, hardest of all, scratch anything, including other diamonds. Table 1 serves as a guide for describing the hardness of minerals.

11. Select three mineral specimens from the set provided by your instructor. Determine the hardness of each mineral, using Table 1 as a guide.

HARDNESS

Specimen A: _____

Specimen B: _____

Specimen C: _____

Cleavage In the crystalline structure of many minerals, some chemical bonds are weaker than others. When minerals are stressed, they tend to break (cleave) along these planes of weak bonding, a property called **cleavage**. When broken, minerals that exhibit cleavage produce smooth, flat surfaces, called **cleavage planes**, or **cleavage surfaces**.

Cleavage is described by (1) noting the number of **directions of cleavage**, which is the number of different sets of cleavage planes that form on the surfaces of a mineral when it cleaves, and (2) determining the **angle(s)** at which the directions of cleavage meet (Figure 13). Each cleavage surface of a mineral that has a different orientation is counted as a different direction of cleavage. However, when cleavage planes are parallel, they are counted only *once*, as one direction of cleavage. Minerals may have one, two, three, four, or more directions of cleavage (Figure 13).

When minerals such as muscovite, calcite, halite, and fluorite are broken, they display cleavage surfaces that are easily detected. However, other minerals exhibit cleavage planes that consist of multiple offset surfaces that are not as obvious. A reliable way to determine whether a specimen exhibits cleavage is to

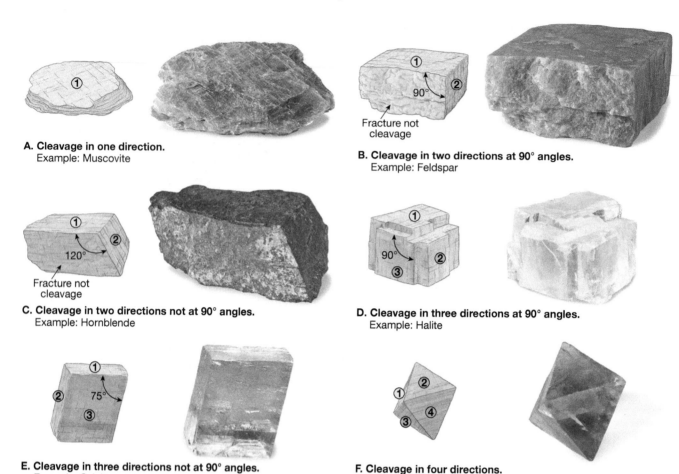

A. Cleavage in one direction.
Example: Muscovite

B. Cleavage in two directions at 90° angles.
Example: Feldspar

C. Cleavage in two directions not at 90° angles.
Example: Hornblende

D. Cleavage in three directions at 90° angles.
Example: Halite

E. Cleavage in three directions not at 90° angles.
Example: Calcite

F. Cleavage in four directions.
Example: Fluorite

Figure 13 Common cleavage directions of minerals. **A.** Basal cleavage produces flat sheets. **B.** This type of prismatic cleavage produces an elongated form with a rectangular cross section. **C.** This type of prismatic cleavage produces an elongated form with a parallelogram cross section. **D.** Cubic cleavage produces cubes or parts of cubes. **E.** Rhombohedral cleavage produces rhombohedrons. **F.** Octahedral cleavage produces octahedrons.

rotate it in bright light and look for flat surfaces that reflect light.

Do not confuse cleavage with crystal shape. When a mineral exhibits cleavage, it will break into pieces that all have the same geometry. By contrast, the smooth-sided quartz crystals shown in Figure 7 illustrate crystal shape rather than cleavage. If broken, quartz crystals fracture into shapes that do not resemble one another or the original crystals.

12. Describe the cleavage of the mineral shown in Figure 14A.

   _____

13. Refer to the photograph in Figure 14B, which shows a mineral that has several smooth, flat cleavage surfaces, to complete the following.

   a. How many cleavage planes or surfaces are present on the specimen?

      Number of cleavage planes: _____

A. Muscovite

B. Calcite

Figure 14 Identifying cleavage.

b. How many directions of cleavage are present on the specimen?

Number of directions of cleavage: _____

c. The cleavage directions meet at (90-degree angles *or* angles other than 90 degrees).

Degrees of cleavage angles: _____

14. Select one mineral specimen supplied by your instructor that exhibits more than one direction of cleavage. How many directions of cleavage does it have? What are the angles of its cleavage?

Number of directions of cleavage: _____

Degrees of cleavage angles: _____

Fracture   Minerals that do not exhibit cleavage when broken are said to **fracture** (Figure 15). Fractures are described using terms such as *irregular, splintery,* or *conchoidal* (smooth, curved surfaces resembling broken glass). Some minerals may cleave in one or two directions and fracture in another.

Density and Specific Gravity

Density is defined as mass per unit volume and is expressed in grams per cubic centimeter (g/cm^3). Mineralogists also use a related measure called *specific gravity* to describe the density of minerals. **Specific gravity (SG)** is a number representing the ratio of a mineral's weight to the weight of an equal volume of water. Water has a specific gravity of 1.

Most common rock-forming minerals have specific gravities of between 2 and 3. For example, quartz has a specific gravity of 2.7. By contrast, some metallic minerals such as pyrite, native copper, and magnetite are more than twice as dense as quartz and thus are considered to have a high specific gravity. Galena, an ore of lead, is even more dense, with a specific gravity of about 7.5.

With a little practice, you can estimate the specific gravity of a mineral by hefting it in your hand. Ask yourself whether the mineral feels about as "heavy" as

Figure 16   A variety of magnetite, lodestone, is like a magnet and will attract iron objects.

similar-sized rocks you have handled. If the answer is "yes," the specific gravity of the sample is likely between 2.5 and 3. (*Note:* Exercise 23, "The Metric System, Measurements, and Scientific Inquiry," contains a simple experiment for estimating the specific gravity of a solid.)

15. Hefting each specimen supplied by your instructor. Identify the minerals from this group that exhibit high specific gravities.

a. How many minerals have a high specific gravity? _____

b. Of those with a high SG, did most of them have a metallic or nonmetallic luster? _____

Other Properties of Minerals

Magnetism   Magnetism is characteristic of minerals, such as magnetite, that have a high iron content and are attracted by a magnet. One variety of magnetite called *lodestone* is magnetic and will pick up small objects such as pins and paper clips (Figure 16).

Taste   The mineral halite has a "salty" taste.

> **CAUTION:** Do not taste any minerals or any other materials unless you know it is *absolutely* safe to do so.

Odor   A few minerals have distinctive odors. For example, minerals that are compounds of sulfur smell like rotten eggs when rubbed vigorously on a streak plate.

Feel   The mineral talc often feels "soapy," and the mineral graphite has a "greasy" feel.

Striations   Striations are closely spaced, fine lines on the crystal faces of some minerals. Certain plagioclase

A. Irregular fracture   **B. Conchoidal fracture**

Figure 15   Minerals that do not exhibit cleavage are said to fracture.

Figure 17 These parallel lines, called *striations*, are a distinguishing characteristic of the plagioclase feldspars.

feldspar minerals exhibit striations on one cleavage surface (Figure 17).

Reaction to Dilute Hydrochloric Acid A very small drop of dilute hydrochloric acid, when placed on the surface of certain minerals, will cause them to "fizz" (effervesce) as carbon dioxide is released (Figure 18). The acid test is used to identify the *carbonate minerals*, especially the mineral calcite ($CaCo_3$), the most common carbonate mineral.

> **CAUTION:** Hydrochloric acid can discolor, decompose, and disintegrate mineral and rock samples. Use the acid only after you have received specific instructions on its use from your instructor. Never taste minerals that have had acid placed on them.

Identification of Minerals

Now that you are familiar with the physical properties of minerals, you are ready to identify the minerals supplied by your instructor. To complete this activity, you need the Mineral Data Sheet (Figure 19) and the Mineral Identification Key (Figure 20).

The mineral identification key divides minerals into three primary categories: (1) those with metallic luster, (2) those with nonmetallic luster that are dark colored, (3) and those with nonmetallic luster that are light colored. Hardness is used as a secondary identifying factor. As you complete this exercise, remember that the objective is to learn the *procedure* for identifying minerals through *observation* and *data collection* rather than simply to name the minerals.

Figure 18 Calcite reacting with dilute hydrochloric acid. (Photo by Chip Clark)

16. Identify the specimens supplied by your instructor, using the following steps:

    Step 1: Leaving enough space for each mineral, number a piece of paper (up to the number of samples you've been assigned) and place your specimens on the paper.

    Step 2: Select a specimen and determine its physical properties by using the tools provided (glass plate, streak plate, magnet, etc.).

    Step 3: List the properties of that specimen on the Mineral Data Sheet (Figure 19).

    Step 4: Use the Mineral Identification Key (Figure 20) as a resource to identify the specimen.

    Repeat steps 2 through 4 until all samples have been identified.

    In the following section you will examine some common rock-forming minerals and selected economic minerals. This will provide you with the information needed to complete the last column of the mineral data sheet (Figure 19).

MINERAL DATA SHEET #1

Sample number	Luster	Hardness	Color	Streak	Fracture or Cleavage (number of directions and angles)	Other Properties	Name	Economic Use or Rock-forming

Refer to the section on "Mineral Groups" to complete this part

Figure 19 Mineral data sheet.

MINERAL DATA SHEET #2

Sample number	Luster	Hardness	Color	Streak	Fracture or Cleavage (number of directions and angles)	Other Properties	Name	Economic Use or Rock-forming

Refer to the section on "Mineral Groups" to complete this part

Figure 19 Mineral data sheet (*continued*)

MINERAL DATA SHEET #3

Sample number	Luster	Hardness	Color	Streak	Fracture or Cleavage (number of directions and angles)	Other Properties	Name	Economic Use or Rock-forming

Refer to the section on "Mineral Groups" to complete this part

Figure 19 Mineral data sheet (*continued*)

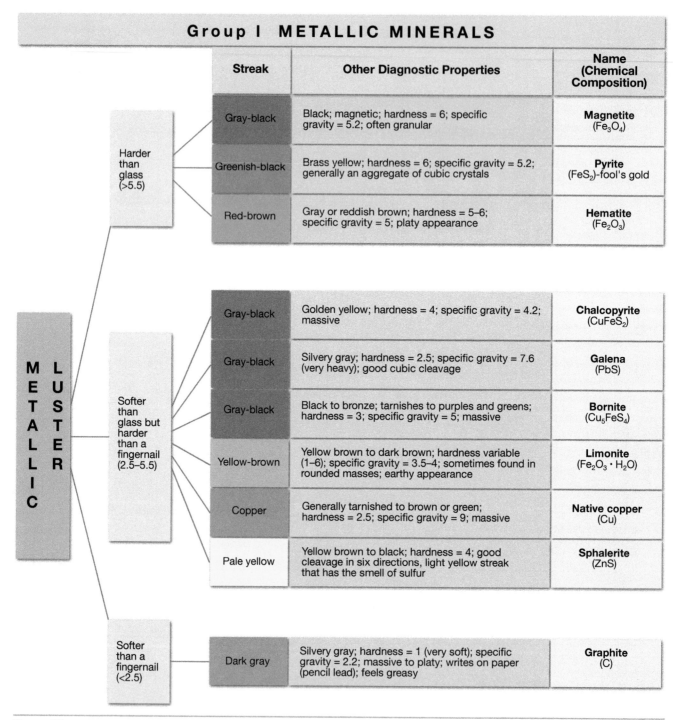

Group I METALLIC MINERALS

Streak	Other Diagnostic Properties	Name (Chemical Composition)
Harder than glass (>5.5)		
Gray-black	Black; magnetic; hardness = 6; specific gravity = 5.2; often granular	**Magnetite** (Fe_3O_4)
Greenish-black	Brass yellow; hardness = 6; specific gravity = 5.2; generally an aggregate of cubic crystals	**Pyrite** (FeS_2)-fool's gold
Red-brown	Gray or reddish brown; hardness = 5–6; specific gravity = 5; platy appearance	**Hematite** (Fe_2O_3)
Softer than glass but harder than a fingernail (2.5–5.5)		
Gray-black	Golden yellow; hardness = 4; specific gravity = 4.2; massive	**Chalcopyrite** ($CuFeS_2$)
Gray-black	Silvery gray; hardness = 2.5; specific gravity = 7.6 (very heavy); good cubic cleavage	**Galena** (PbS)
Gray-black	Black to bronze; tarnishes to purples and greens; hardness = 3; specific gravity = 5; massive	**Bornite** (Cu_5FeS_4)
Yellow-brown	Yellow brown to dark brown; hardness variable (1–6); specific gravity = 3.5–4; sometimes found in rounded masses; earthy appearance	**Limonite** ($Fe_2O_3 \cdot H_2O$)
Copper	Generally tarnished to brown or green; hardness = 2.5; specific gravity = 9; massive	**Native copper** (Cu)
Pale yellow	Yellow brown to black; hardness = 4; good cleavage in six directions, light yellow streak that has the smell of sulfur	**Sphalerite** (ZnS)
Softer than a fingernail (<2.5)		
Dark gray	Silvery gray; hardness = 1 (very soft); specific gravity = 2.2; massive to platy; writes on paper (pencil lead); feels greasy	**Graphite** (C)

METALLIC LUSTER

Figure 20 Mineral identification key.

Mineral Groups

More than 4000 minerals have been named, and several new ones are identified each year. Fortunately for students who are beginning to study minerals, no more than a few dozen are abundant! Collectively, these few make up most of the rocks of Earth's crust and, as such, are referred to as the **rock-forming minerals**.

Although less abundant, many other minerals are used extensively in the manufacture of products and are called **economic minerals**. However, rock-forming minerals and economic minerals are not mutually exclusive groups. When found in large deposits, some rock-forming minerals are economically significant. For example, the mineral calcite, the primary component of the sedimentary rock limestone, has many uses, including the production of concrete.

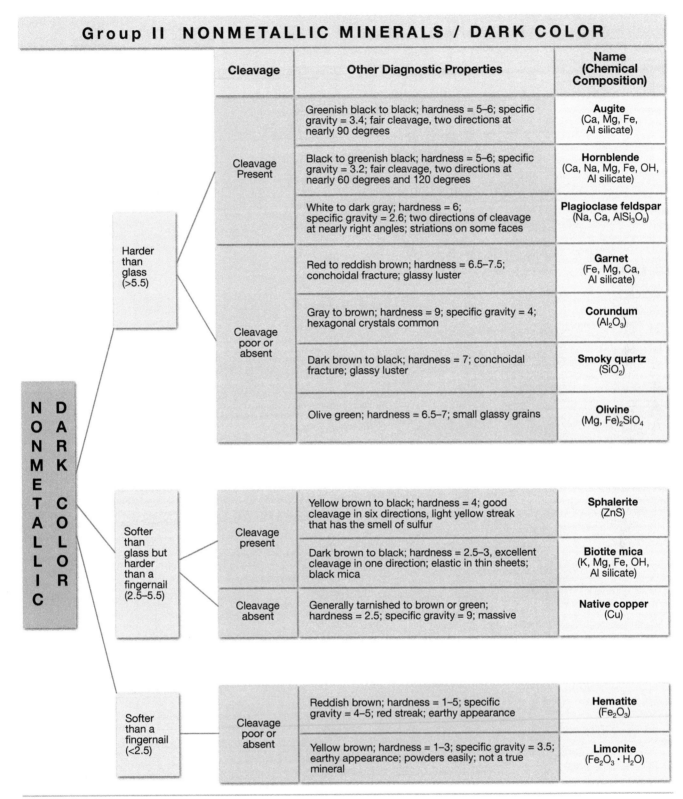

Group II NONMETALLIC MINERALS / DARK COLOR

	Cleavage	Other Diagnostic Properties	Name (Chemical Composition)
Harder than glass (>5.5)	Cleavage Present	Greenish black to black; hardness = 5–6; specific gravity = 3.4; fair cleavage, two directions at nearly 90 degrees	**Augite** (Ca, Mg, Fe, Al silicate)
		Black to greenish black; hardness = 5–6; specific gravity = 3.2; fair cleavage, two directions at nearly 60 degrees and 120 degrees	**Hornblende** (Ca, Na, Mg, Fe, OH, Al silicate)
		White to dark gray; hardness = 6; specific gravity = 2.6; two directions of cleavage at nearly right angles; striations on some faces	**Plagioclase feldspar** (Na, Ca, AlSi₃O₈)
	Cleavage poor or absent	Red to reddish brown; hardness = 6.5–7.5; conchoidal fracture; glassy luster	**Garnet** (Fe, Mg, Ca, Al silicate)
		Gray to brown; hardness = 9; specific gravity = 4; hexagonal crystals common	**Corundum** (Al₂O₃)
		Dark brown to black; hardness = 7; conchoidal fracture; glassy luster	**Smoky quartz** (SiO₂)
		Olive green; hardness = 6.5–7; small glassy grains	**Olivine** (Mg, Fe)₂SiO₄
Softer than glass but harder than a fingernail (2.5–5.5)	Cleavage present	Yellow brown to black; hardness = 4; good cleavage in six directions, light yellow streak that has the smell of sulfur	**Sphalerite** (ZnS)
		Dark brown to black; hardness = 2.5–3, excellent cleavage in one direction; elastic in thin sheets; black mica	**Biotite mica** (K, Mg, Fe, OH, Al silicate)
	Cleavage absent	Generally tarnished to brown or green; hardness = 2.5; specific gravity = 9; massive	**Native copper** (Cu)
Softer than a fingernail (<2.5)	Cleavage poor or absent	Reddish brown; hardness = 1–5; specific gravity = 4–5; red streak; earthy appearance	**Hematite** (Fe₂O₃)
		Yellow brown; hardness = 1–3; specific gravity = 3.5; earthy appearance; powders easily; not a true mineral	**Limonite** (Fe₂O₃ · H₂O)

(The leftmost column label reads vertically: **NONMETALLIC DARK COLOR**)

Figure 20 Mineral identification key (*continued*)

Important Rock-Forming Minerals

Feldspar Group Feldspar is the most abundant mineral group and is found in many igneous, sedimentary, and metamorphic rocks (Figure 21). One group of feldspar minerals contains potassium ions in its crystalline structure and is referred to as *potassium feldspar*. The other group, called *plagioclase feldspar*, contains calcium and/or sodium ions (Figure 21). All feldspar minerals have two directions of cleavage that meet at 90-degree angles and are relatively hard (6 on the

Group III NONMETALLIC MINERALS / LIGHT COLOR

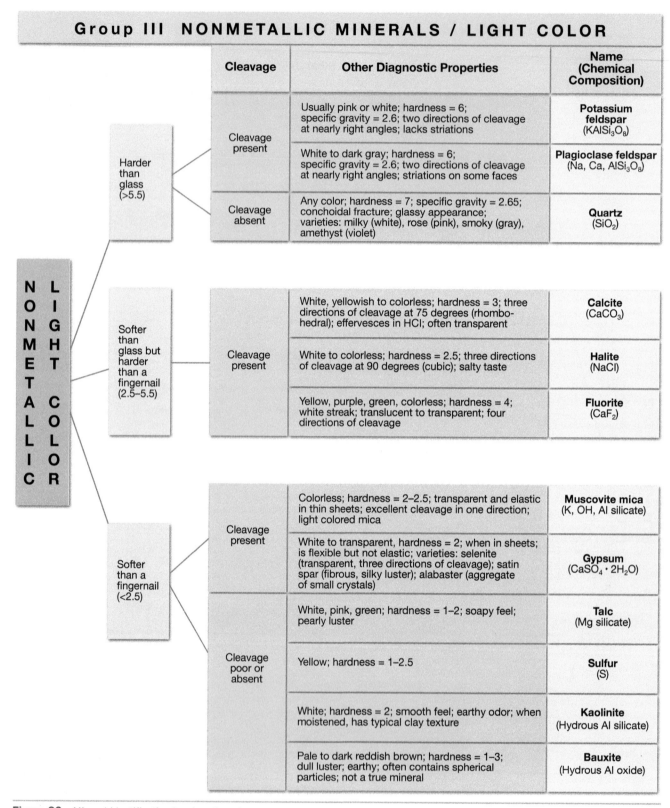

NONMETALLIC LIGHT COLOR		Cleavage	Other Diagnostic Properties	Name (Chemical Composition)
	Harder than glass (>5.5)	Cleavage present	Usually pink or white; hardness = 6; specific gravity = 2.6; two directions of cleavage at nearly right angles; lacks striations	**Potassium feldspar** ($KAlSi_3O_8$)
			White to dark gray; hardness = 6; specific gravity = 2.6; two directions of cleavage at nearly right angles; striations on some faces	**Plagioclase feldspar** ($Na, Ca, AlSi_3O_8$)
		Cleavage absent	Any color; hardness = 7; specific gravity = 2.65; conchoidal fracture; glassy appearance; varieties: milky (white), rose (pink), smoky (gray), amethyst (violet)	**Quartz** (SiO_2)
	Softer than glass but harder than a fingernail (2.5–5.5)	Cleavage present	White, yellowish to colorless; hardness = 3; three directions of cleavage at 75 degrees (rhombohedral); effervesces in HCl; often transparent	**Calcite** ($CaCO_3$)
			White to colorless; hardness = 2.5; three directions of cleavage at 90 degrees (cubic); salty taste	**Halite** ($NaCl$)
			Yellow, purple, green, colorless; hardness = 4; white streak; translucent to transparent; four directions of cleavage	**Fluorite** (CaF_2)
	Softer than a fingernail (<2.5)	Cleavage present	Colorless; hardness = 2–2.5; transparent and elastic in thin sheets; excellent cleavage in one direction; light colored mica	**Muscovite mica** (K, OH, Al silicate)
			White to transparent, hardness = 2; when in sheets; is flexible but not elastic; varieties: selenite (transparent, three directions of cleavage); satin spar (fibrous, silky luster); alabaster (aggregate of small crystals)	**Gypsum** ($CaSO_4 \cdot 2H_2O$)
		Cleavage poor or absent	White, pink, green; hardness = 1–2; soapy feel; pearly luster	**Talc** (Mg silicate)
			Yellow; hardness = 1–2.5	**Sulfur** (S)
			White; hardness = 2; smooth feel; earthy odor; when moistened, has typical clay texture	**Kaolinite** (Hydrous Al silicate)
			Pale to dark reddish brown; hardness = 1–3; dull luster; earthy; often contains spherical particles; not a true mineral	**Bauxite** (Hydrous Al oxide)

Figure 20 Mineral identification key (*continued*)

Mohs scale). The only reliable way to physically distinguish the feldspars is to look for striations that are present on some cleavage surfaces of plagioclase feldspar (see Figure 17) but do not appear in potassium feldspar.

Quartz Quartz is a major constituent of many igneous, sedimentary, and metamorphic rocks. Quartz is found in a wide variety of colors (caused by impurities), is quite hard (7 on the Mohs scale), and exhibits conchoidal fracture when broken (Figure 22). Pure

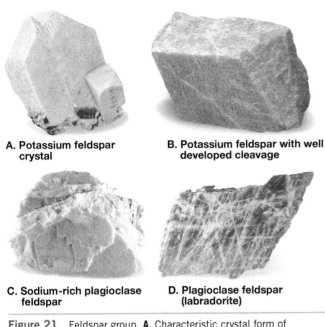

A. Potassium feldspar crystal

B. Potassium feldspar with well developed cleavage

C. Sodium-rich plagioclase feldspar

D. Plagioclase feldspar (labradorite)

Figure 21 Feldspar group. **A.** Characteristic crystal form of plagioclase feldspar. **B.** Like this sample, most pink feldspar belongs to the potassium feldspar subgroup. **C.** Most sodium-rich plagioclase feldspar is light colored and has a porcelain luster. **D.** Calcium-rich plagioclase feldspar tends to be gray, blue-gray, or black in color. Labradorite, the variety shown here, exhibits iridescence.

quartz is clear, and if allowed to grow without interference, it will develop hexagonal crystals with pyramid-shaped ends (see Figure 7).

Mica Muscovite and *biotite* are the two most abundant members of the mica family. Both have excellent

A. Smoky quartz

B. Rose quartz

C. Milky quartz

D. Jasper

Figure 22 Quartz is one of the most common minerals and has many varieties. **A.** Smoky quartz is commonly found in coarse-grained igneous rocks. **B.** Rose quartz owes its color to small amounts of titanium. **C.** Milky quartz often occurs in veins that occasionally contain gold. **D.** Jasper is a variety of quartz composed of minute crystals.

A. Muscovite

B. Biotite

Figure 23 Two common micas: **A.** muscovite and **B.** biotite.

Kaolinite

Figure 24 Kaolinite, a common clay mineral.

Olivine

Figure 25 Olivine.

cleavage in one direction and are relatively soft (2.5 to 3 on the Mohs scale) (Figure 23).

Clay Minerals Most clay minerals originate as products of chemical weathering and make up much of the surface material we call soil. Clay minerals also account for nearly half of the volume of sedimentary rocks (Figure 24).

Olivine Olivine is an important group of minerals that are major constituents of dark-colored igneous rocks and make up much of Earth's upper mantle. Olivine is black to olive green in color, has a glassy luster, and exhibits conchoidal fracture (Figure 25).

A. Augite   **B. Hornblende**

Figure 26 These dark-colored silicate minerals are common constituents of igneous rocks: **A.** augite and **B.** hornblende.

Pyroxene Group The *pyroxenes* are a group of silicate minerals that are important components of dark-colored igneous rocks. The most common member, *augite*, is a black, opaque mineral with two directions of cleavage that meet at nearly 90-degree angles (Figure 26A).

Amphibole Group *Hornblende* is the most common member of the amphibole group and is usually dark green to black in color (Figure 26B). Except for its cleavage angles, which are about 60 degrees and 120 degrees, it is very similar in appearance to augite. Found in igneous rocks, hornblende makes up the dark portion of otherwise light-colored rocks.

Calcite *Calcite*, a very abundant mineral, is the primary constituent in the sedimentary rock limestone and the metamorphic rock marble. A relatively soft mineral (3 on the Mohs scale), calcite has three directions of cleavage that meet at 75-degree angles (see Figure 14B).

17. When feldspar minerals are found in igneous rocks, they tend to occur as elongated, rectangular crystals. By contrast, quartz (most commonly the smoky and milky varieties) usually occurs as irregular or rounded grains that have a glassy texture. Which of the crystals (A, B, C, or D) in the igneous rocks shown in Figure 27 are feldspar crystals and which are quartz?

    Feldspar: _____

    Quartz: _____

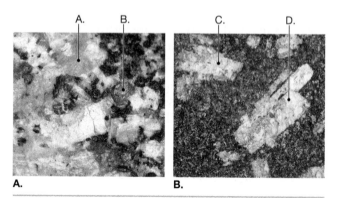

Figure 27 Identifying crystals of feldspar and quartz in coarse-grained igneous rocks.

Table 2   Economic Minerals

MINERAL	INDUSTRIAL AND COMMERCIAL USES
Calcite	Cement; soil conditioning
Chalcopyrite	Major ore of copper
Corundum	Gemstones, sandpaper
Diamond	Gemstones, drill bits
Fluorite	Used in steel manufacturing, toothpaste
Galena	Major ore of lead
Graphite	Pencil lead; lubricant
Gypsum	Wallboard; plaster
Halite	Table salt, road salt
Hematite	Ore of iron; pigment
Kaolinite	Ceramics; porcelain
Magnetite	Ore of iron
Muscovite	Insulator in electrical applications
Quartz	Primary ingredient in glass
Sphalerite	Major ore of zinc
Sulfur	Sulfa drugs; sulfuric acid
Sylvite	Potassium fertilizers
Talc	Paint, cosmetics

Economic Minerals

Many of the minerals selected for this exercise are metallic minerals that are mined to support our modern society. In addition, nonmetallic minerals such as fluorite, halite, and gypsum have economic value. Table 2 provides a list of some economic minerals and their industrial and commercial uses.

18. Complete the last column in the mineral data sheet (Figure 19) by indicating "rock-forming" or by listing the economic use of the samples used in this exercise (see Table 2).

Companion Website

The companion website provides numerous opportunities to explore and reinforce the topics of this lab exercise. To access this useful tool, follow these steps:

1. Go to www.mygeoscienceplace.com.
2. Click on "Books Available" at the top of the page.
3. Click on the cover of *Applications and Investigations in Earth Science, 7e.*
4. Select the chapter you want to access. Options are listed in the left column ("Introduction," "Web-based Activities," "Related Websites," and "Field Trips").

The Study of Minerals

Name _____   Course/Section _____

Date _____   Due Date _____

1. Name the physical property (hardness, color, streak, etc.) described by each of the following statements.

DESCRIPTION	PHYSICAL PROPERTY
Breaks along smooth planes:	_____
Scratches glass:	_____
Shines like a metal:	_____
Red powder:	_____
Looks like broken glass:	_____

2. What term is used to describe the shape of a mineral that has three directions of cleavage that intersect at 90 degrees?

_____

3. Describe the cleavage of the minerals listed below.

MINERAL	CLEAVAGE
Muscovite:	_____
Calcite:	_____
Halite:	_____

4. Describe the cleavage of the feldspar minerals (potassium feldspar and plagioclase feldspar).

_____

Number of directions of cleavage: _____

Degrees of cleavage angles: _____

5. What physical property most distinguishes biotite mica from muscovite mica?

_____

6. Name a mineral that exhibits the physical properties listed below. (Use the photos in this exercise, if needed.)

PROPERTY	MINERAL
One direction of cleavage:	_____
Striations:	_____
Multiple colors:	_____
Cubic cleavage:	_____
Nonmetallic, vitreous Luster:	_____
Fracture:	_____
Metallic luster:	_____

7. Figure 28 illustrates the common crystal form of the mineral fluorite and the characteristic shape of a cleaved sample of fluorite. Identify each specimen (A *or* B) next to its appropriate description below.

Crystal form of fluorite: _____

Cleavage of fluorite: _____

A.   B.

Figure 28 Comparing crystal shape and cleavage.

8. Refer to the photo in Figure 29 to complete the following:

   a. Describe the crystal form of this specimen.

   _____

   b. What term is used to describe the lines on this sample?

   _____

   c. Based on what you can discern from this photo, use the mineral identification key (Figure 20) to name this mineral.

   _____

9. A photo of *agate*, a variety of quartz composed of minute crystals, is provided in Figure 30. Based on this image, describe the habit of this sample.

   _____

10. If a mineral can be scratched by a penny but not by a human fingernail, what is its hardness on the Mohs scale?

    Hardness: _____

11. What term is used to describe the tenacity of muscovite?

    Tenacity of muscovite: _____

12. Use the mineral identification key (Figure 20) to identify a mineral that is nonmetallic, colored, lacks cleavage, and is green in color.

    Mineral name: _____

Figure 29 Identifying mineral properties through observation.

Figure 30 What habit does this sample display?

13. For each mineral listed below, list at least one diagnostic property. (Refer to your mineral data sheet in Figure 19, if necessary.)

MINERAL NAME	DIAGNOSTIC PROPERTY
Halite:	_____
Galena:	_____
Magnetite:	_____
Muscovite:	_____
Hematite:	_____
Fluorite:	_____
Talc:	_____
Graphite:	_____
Calcite:	_____

14. List the two most common rock-forming mineral groups.

    _____

    _____

15. Provide an economic use for each mineral listed below:

    Galena: _____

    Hematite: _____

    Graphite: _____

    Sphalerite: _____

    Gypsum: _____

    Calcite: _____

Rocks and the Rock Cycle

Objectives

Completion of this exercise will prepare you to:

A. Determine whether rocks are igneous, sedimentary, or metamorphic.

B. Describe what the texture of a rock indicates about its history.

C. Name the dominant mineral(s) found in common igneous, sedimentary, and metamorphic rocks.

D. Identify the environments in which sediments are deposited.

E. Use a classification key to identify rocks.

F. Recognize and name some common rocks.

Materials

metric ruler	igneous rocks
glass plate	sedimentary rocks
iron nail	metamorphic rocks
dilute hydrochloric acid	hand lens

Introduction

Most **rocks** are aggregates (mixtures) of mineral grains or fragments (gravel, sand, and silt) of preexisting rocks. However, there are some important exceptions including *obsidian*, which is a rock made of volcanic glass (a non-crystalline substance), and *coal*, which is a rock made of decayed plant material (an organic substance).

Rocks are classified into three groups—igneous, sedimentary, and metamorphic—based on the processes by which they were formed. One very useful device for understanding rock types and the geologic processes that transform one rock type into another is the **rock cycle** (Figure 1). Examine the rock cycle as you read the following descriptions of each rock group and pay particular attention to the processes that formed them.

Igneous rocks are the solidified products of once-molten material that was created by melting in the upper mantle or crust. Geologists call molten rock **magma** when it is found at depth and **lava** when it erupts at Earth's surface. The distinguishing feature of most igneous rocks is the interlocking arrangement of their mineral crystals that develops as the molten material cools and solidifies. *Intrusive* igneous rocks form below Earth's surface from magma, and *extrusive* igneous rocks form at the surface from lava. Volcanism produces a variety of distinctive rock structures (Figure 2).

Sedimentary rocks form at or near Earth's surface from the products of *weathering*. This material, called **sediment**, is transported by erosional agents (water, wind, or ice) as solid particles or ions in solution to their site of deposition. The process of **lithification** (meaning "to turn to stone") transforms the sediment into hard rock. Sedimentary rocks cover much of Earth's surface and may contain organic matter (oil, gas, and coal) and fossils. The layering that develops when sediment is deposited is the most recognizable feature of sedimentary rocks. These layers, called **strata**, or **beds**, usually accumulate in nearly horizontal sheets that can be as thin as a piece of paper or tens of meters thick (Figure 3).

Metamorphic rocks are produced from preexisting igneous, sedimentary, or other metamorphic rocks that have been subjected to conditions within Earth that are significantly different from those under which the rock originally formed. *Metamorphism*, the process that causes the transformation, generally occurs at depths where both the temperatures and pressures are significantly higher than at Earth's surface.

Rock Textures and Compositions

The task of distinguishing the three rock groups and naming individual samples relies heavily on the ability to recognize their *textures* and *compositions*.

Texture refers to the shape, arrangement, and size of mineral grains in a rock. The shape and arrangement

ROCK CYCLE

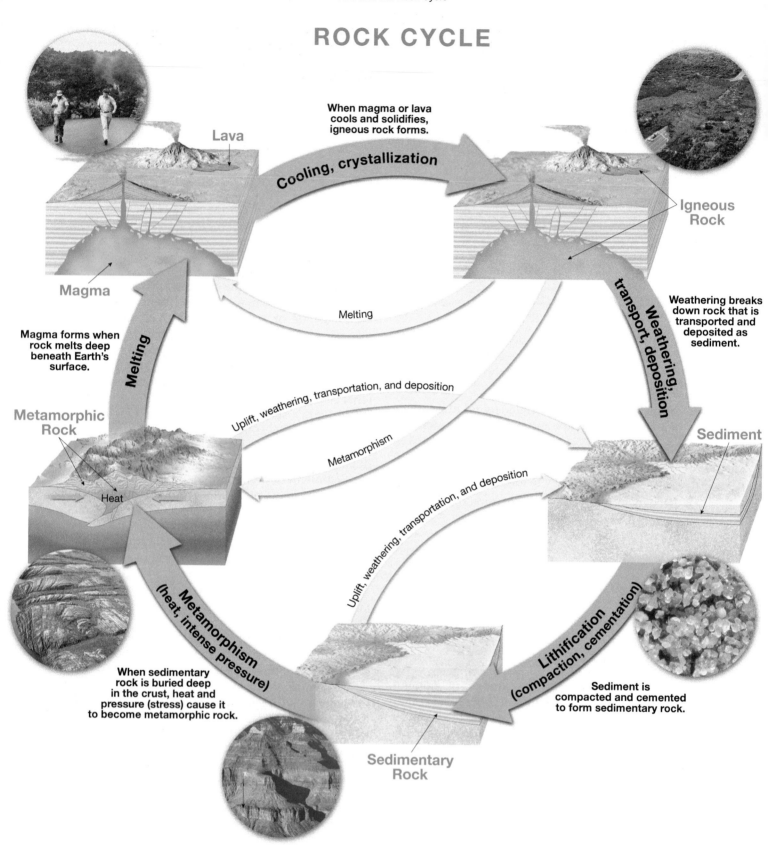

When magma or lava cools and solidifies, igneous rock forms.

Lava

Cooling, crystallization

Igneous Rock

Melting

Magma

Magma forms when rock melts deep beneath Earth's surface.

Melting

Weathering breaks down rock that is transported and deposited as sediment.

Weathering, transport, deposition

Metamorphic Rock

Uplift, weathering, transportation, and deposition

Metamorphism

Sediment

Heat

Uplift, weathering, transportation, and deposition

Metamorphism (heat, intense pressure)

Lithification (compaction, cementation)

When sedimentary rock is buried deep in the crust, heat and pressure (stress) cause it to become metamorphic rock.

Sediment is compacted and cemented to form sedimentary rock.

Sedimentary Rock

Figure 1 Over long spans, rocks are constantly forming, changing, and reforming. The rock cycle helps us understand the origin of the three basic rock groups. Arrows represent processes that link each group to the others.

A. Lava flows

B. Volcanic bombs

C. Vesicular texture

D. Columnar jointing

Figure 2 Volcanism produces a variety of distinctive rock structures. **A.** Lava flow that consists of rough jagged blocks sits atop a flow that exhibits a smooth ropy surface. **B.** A volcanic bomb produced when molten lava was hurled from a volcano. **C.** Vesicles are somewhat spherical voids left by gas bubbles that form as lava solidifies. **D.** Columns in a lava flow that formed by contraction and fracture as the lava cooled.

of mineral grains provide clues to whether a rock is igneous, sedimentary, or metamorphic.

Composition refers to the abundance and type of minerals found in a rock. Large mineral grains can often be identified by sight or by their physical properties, while a hand lens or microscope may be needed to identify small mineral grains. In addition, a few

minerals can be identified by a particular diagnostic property. For example, rocks composed of the mineral calcite fizz when a drop of dilute hydrochloric acid (HCl) is applied.

Rock Classification

One of the first steps in rock identification is to determine the group to which a sample belongs. Every rock has characteristics that aid in determining whether it is igneous, sedimentary, or metamorphic. Igneous rocks generally consist of randomly oriented, interlocking crystals of two or more different minerals and tend to be relatively hard. A few igneous rocks exhibit easily recognized properties such as having the appearance of dark broken glass or exhibiting many bubble-shaped holes.

Most sedimentary rocks, on the other hand, are composed of weathered rock debris (silt, sand, pebbles, and gravel) that is often easily identified in a hand sample. Other sedimentary rocks are recognized because they contain shells or plant debris that has been compacted or cemented into a solid mass. Some sedimentary rocks form when material dissolved in water precipitates to generate a rock composed of intergrown crystals—distinguishable from crystalline igneous rocks because they tend to be composed of easily identifiable minerals—calcite, halite, or gypsum.

Metamorphic rocks are produced from preexisting rocks by heat and pressure, and they are sometimes difficult to distinguish from their parent rock. Some

Figure 3 Sedimentary layers, called strata, or beds.

Figure 4 Highly deformed metamorphic rock.

metamorphic rocks, however, exhibit a characteristic parallel alignment of flat crystals or elongated crystals that can be diagnostic. Others show clear evidence of having been deformed by folding (Figure 4).

The origin of a particular rock may also be revealed by the presence of certain minerals within it. For example, halite and gypsum form when saltwater evaporates and, thus, are found almost exclusively in sedimentary rocks. When mica crystals are abundant, it is a good indication that a rock is metamorphic. The presence of quartz, however, is of no value in determining rock type because it is common in all three rock groups.

Examine the close-up images of the rock samples in Figure 5 to answer the following questions.

1. Which of the samples (A–H) are composed of weathered rock material or shells (fossils) that have been lithified?

   Sample(s): _____

2. Which of the samples you listed in question 1 is/are composed mainly of rounded rock fragments?

   Sample(s): _____

3. Which of the samples you listed in question 1 is/are composed mainly of angular rock fragments?

   Sample(s): _____

4. Which of the samples you listed in question 2 is/are composed of sand-size particles?

   Sample(s): _____

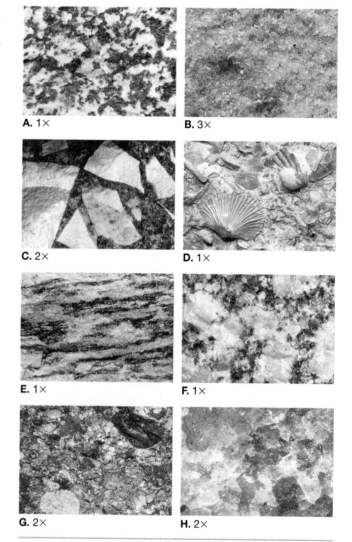

A. 1×

B. 3×

C. 2×

D. 1×

E. 1×

F. 1×

G. 2×

H. 2×

Figure 5 Comparison of igneous, sedimentary, and metamorphic rocks.

22

5. Which of the samples (A–H) are crystalline—composed of interlocking crystals?

   Sample(s): _____

6. Which of the samples you listed in question 5 consists of randomly oriented interlocking crystals of two or more different minerals?

   Sample(s): _____

7. The samples you listed in question 6 belong to which rock group?

   Rock type: _____

8. Which of the samples (A–H) has/have the mineral crystals aligned, or arranged so they are oriented in the same direction?

   Sample(s): _____

9. Which of the samples you listed in question 5 consist of interlocking crystals of what appears to be the same mineral?

   Sample(s): _____

10. Classify the rocks in the samples (A–H in) as either igneous, sedimentary, or metamorphic. (Hint: Sample H has a salty taste.)

    Igneous: _____

    Sedimentary: _____

    Metamorphic: _____

Igneous Rocks

Igneous rocks are generated by cooling and crystallization of molten rock. The interlocking network of silicate minerals that develop as the molten material cools gives most igneous rocks their distinctive crystalline appearance.

Textures of Igneous Rocks

The rate at which magma cools determines the size of the interlocking crystals found in igneous rocks. The slower the cooling rate, the larger the mineral crystals.

Coarse-Grained (Phaneritic) Texture When a large mass of magma solidifies at depth, it cools slowly and forms igneous rocks that exhibit a **coarse-grained texture**. These rocks have intergrown crystals that are roughly equal in size and large enough that the individual minerals within can be identified with the unaided eye. A hand lens or binocular microscope can greatly assist in mineral identification.

Fine-Grained (Aphanitic) Texture Igneous rocks that form when molten material cools rapidly at the surface or as small masses within the upper crust exhibit a **fine-grained texture**. Fine-grained igneous rocks are composed of individual crystals that are too small to be identified without strong magnification.

Porphyritic Texture A **porphyritic texture** results when molten rock cools in two different environments. The resulting rock consists of larger crystals embedded in a matrix of smaller crystals. The larger crystals are termed *phenocrysts*, and the smaller, surrounding crystals are called *groundmass*, or *matrix*.

Glassy Texture During explosive volcanic eruptions, molten rock is ejected into the atmosphere, where it is quenched very quickly. When the material solidifies before the atoms arrange themselves into an orderly crystalline structure, the rocks exhibit a **glassy texture** that resembles manufactured glass.

Fragmental, or Pyroclastic Texture Volcanoes sometimes blast fine ash, molten blobs, and/or angular blocks torn from the walls of the vent into the air during an eruption. Igneous rocks composed of these rock fragments have a **fragmental**, or **pyroclastic texture**.

Vesicular Texture Common features of some fine-grained extrusive igneous rocks are the voids left by gas bubbles that escape as lava solidifies. These somewhat spherical openings are called *vesicles*, and the rocks that contain them have a **vesicular texture**.

Use the close-up photos of igneous rocks in Figure 6 to answer the following questions.

11. Which sample(s) (A–H) exhibit a porphyritic texture?

    Sample(s): _____

12. Of the sample(s) you listed in question 11, what terms are used to denote the larger crystals and the surrounding smaller crystals? Label the larger and smaller crystals on the photo(s).

    Larger crystals: _____

    Smaller crystals: _____

13. Which sample(s) (A–H) exhibit(s) a coarse-grained texture?

    Sample(s): _____

14. Complete the description of the environment in which a *coarse-grained igneous rock* forms by choosing the appropriate terms. (at great depth *or* on the surface) (slowly *or* rapidly) (extrusive *or* intrusive).

    When molten rock solidifies _____, it cools _____, and produces an _____ igneous rock.

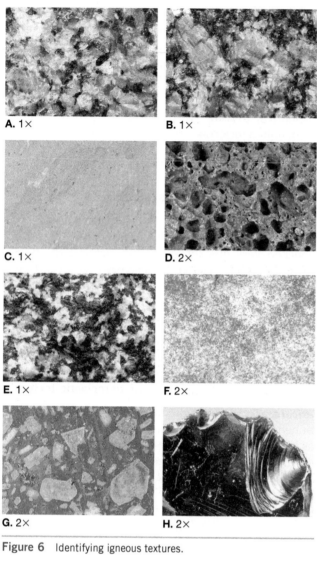

A. 1×   **B.** 1×

C. 1×   **D.** 2×

E. 1×   **F.** 2×

G. 2×   **H.** 2×

Figure 6   Identifying igneous textures.

15. Which of the sample(s) (A–H in Figure 6) exhibit(s) a fine-grained texture?

    Sample(s): _____

16. Complete the description of the environment in which a *fine-grained igneous rock* forms, by choosing the appropriate terms. (at great depth *or* on the surface) (slowly *or* rapidly) (extrusive *or* intrusive).

    When molten rock solidifies _____, it cools _____, and produces an _____ igneous rock.

17. Which of the sample(s) (A–H in Figure 6) exhibit(s) a vesicular texture?

    Sample(s): _____

18. Which sample(s) (A–H in Figure 6) exhibit(s) a glassy texture?

    Sample(s): _____

19. Although Samples A and C (Figure 6) appear different, they have very similar mineral compositions. Briefly explain what accounts for their different appearances.

    _____

    _____

Composition of Igneous Rocks

Despite their significant compositional diversity, igneous rocks (and the magmas from which they form) can be divided into four groups, based on the proportions of light and dark silicate minerals.

Felsic (*granitic*) igneous rocks are composed mainly of the light-colored minerals quartz and potassium feldspars, with lesser amounts of plagioclase feldspar. Recall that feldspar crystals can be identified by their rectangular shapes, flat surfaces, and tendency to be pink, white, or dark gray in color. Quartz grains, on the other hand, are glassy and somewhat rounded and tend to be light gray. Dark-colored minerals account for no more than 15 percent of the minerals in rocks in this group.

Intermediate (*andesitic*) rocks are mixtures of both light-colored minerals (mainly plagioclase feldspar) and dark-colored minerals (mainly amphibole). Dark minerals comprise between 15 percent and 45 percent of these rocks.

Mafic (*basaltic*) rocks contain abundant dark-colored minerals (mainly pyroxene and olivine) that account for between 45 percent and 85 percent of their composition. Plagioclase feldspar makes up the bulk of the remainder.

Ultramafic rocks are composed almost entirely of the dark silicate minerals pyroxene and olivine and are seldom observed at Earth's surface. However, the ultramafic rock peridotite is a major constituent of Earth's upper mantle.

20. On the photo of Sample A in Figure 6, label a quartz crystal.

21. On the photo of Sample B in Figure 6, label a feldspar crystal.

22. What mineral appears to be dominant in Sample A (Figure 6)?

    Dominant mineral: _____

An important skill used in identifying igneous rocks is being able to classify them based on mineral composition—felsic, intermediate, mafic, or ultramafic. However, it is not possible to identify minerals in fine-grained igneous rocks without sophisticated equipment. Further, the dark silicate minerals are often difficult to differentiate—even in coarse-grained rocks. Consequently, geologists working in the field estimate mineralogy using the **color index**, a value based on the percentage of dark silicate minerals (see top of Figure 7). Rocks with a low color index are felsic in composition, whereas those with the highest color index are ultramafic.

It is important to note that although the dark silicate minerals are often black in color, the mineral pyroxene can be dark green, and olivine is often olive green in color. Therefore, rocks with a greenish color have a very high color index and are usually ultramafic in composition.

23. Use Samples A–F in Figure 8 as well as the Color Index located at the top of Figure 7 to complete the following statements:

   a. Sample(s) _____ has/have a felsic (granitic) composition.

   b. Sample(s) _____ has/have an intermediate (andesitic) composition.

   c. Sample(s) _____ has/have a mafic (basaltic) composition.

   d. Sample(s) _____ has/have an ultramafic composition.

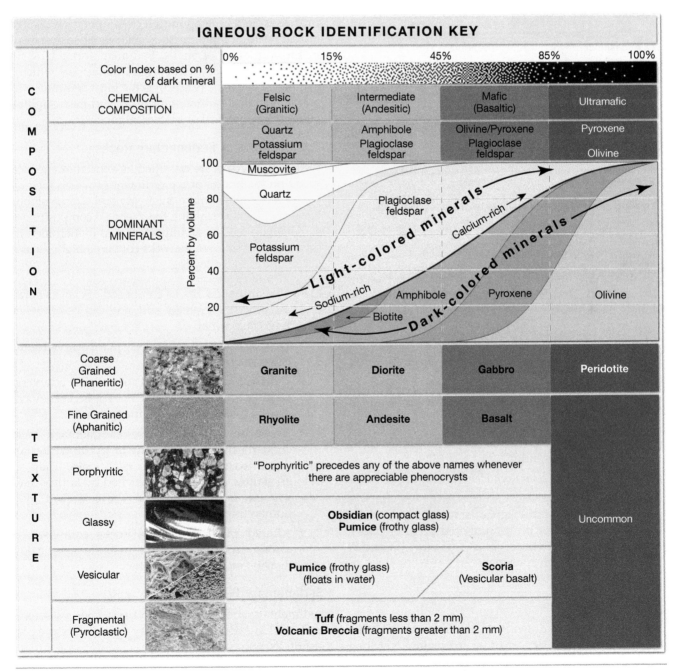

Figure 7 Igneous rock identification key.

A. Rhyolite　　　　　B. Gabbro

C. Andesite porphyry　　　D. Diorite

E. Peridotite　　　　　F. Granite

Figure 8　Hand samples that illustrate igneous compositions.

Igneous Rock Identification

To determine the name of an igneous rock, use the *Igneous Rock Identification Key* found in Figure 7 and follow these steps:

Step 1:　Identify the texture of the rock.

Step 2:　Determine the mineral composition of the rock by:

    a. identifying the abundance of major minerals or

    b. estimating the mineral composition using the color index

Step 3:　Use the *Igneous Rock Identification Key* to name the rock.

24. Place each of the igneous rocks supplied by your instructor on a numbered piece of paper. Then complete the *Igneous Rock Chart* (Figure 9) and name each specimen.

Sedimentary Rocks

Weathering breaks down rock into finer material that is transported and deposited as sediment. Over long periods of time, compaction and cementation turn this sediment into sedimentary rock.

Materials that accumulate as sediment have two principal sources. First, sediments may originate as solid particles from weathered rocks. These particles are called *detritus*, and the rocks that they form are called *detrital sedimentary rocks*. The second major source of sediment is soluble material produced by chemical weathering.

Detrital sedimentary rocks consist of mineral grains or rock fragments derived from mechanical and chemical weathering that are transported and deposited as solid particles. Clay minerals are the most abundant solid products of chemical weathering. Quartz is abundant in detrital rocks because it is extremely durable.

Chemical sedimentary rocks are products of mineral matter that was dissolved in water and later precipitated. Precipitation may occur as a result of processes such as evaporation or temperature change, or as a result of life processes, such as those that result in the formation of shells. Sediment formed by life processes has a *biochemical* origin. Limestone, which is composed of calcite ($CaCO_2$) is the most common mineral in chemical sedimentary rocks and may originate either from chemical or biological processes.

Compositions of Sedimentary Rocks

Sedimentary rocks are classified as detrital or chemical based on the nature of the sediment of which they are composed, rather than their mineral compositions. Nevertheless, determining the chemical composition of sedimentary rocks is an important step in their identification. Most sedimentary rocks contain a high percentage of one of the following:

- **Clay minerals** Rocks composed of clay minerals are very fine grained, soft, and can be scratched with an iron nail.
- **Quartz** Rocks composed of quartz are hard and can scratch glass.
- **Calcite** Rocks composed of calcite effervesce when a drop of dilute HCl is applied. They can also be easily scratched with an iron nail.
- **Evaporite minerals** These sedimentary rocks contain salts, usually halite or gypsum, that are deposited when saltwater evaporates. They are crystalline and can be scratched by an iron nail; gypsum is soft enough to be scratched by a human fingernail.
- **Altered plant fragments** Rocks composed of carbon and other organic material have a low density and are easily broken.

Sedimentary Textures

Sedimentary rocks exhibit two basic textures—*clastic* and *nonclastic*. Rocks that display a **clastic texture** consist of discrete particles that are cemented or compacted together. Clastic textures are further divided based on particle size and shape.

IGNEOUS ROCK CHART

Sample Number	Texture	Color (light- intermediate- dark)	Dominant Minerals	Rock Name

Figure 9 Igneous rock chart.

Rocks that have a **nonclastic texture** are often crystalline and, consist of minerals that form patterns of interlocking crystals. Although crystalline sedimentary rocks can be similar in appearance to some igneous rocks, they tend to consist of minerals—most often calcite, halite, or gypsum—that are easily distinguished from the silicate minerals found in igneous rocks.

Examining Sedimentary Rocks

Carefully examine the common sedimentary rocks shown in Figure 10. Use these photos and the preceding discussion to answer the following questions.

25. What characteristic can be used to distinguish Sample A (conglomerate) from Sample B (breccia)?

26. List the name(s) of the chemical sedimentary rocks that clearly exhibit a clastic texture.

27. Samples C, O, P, and Q are all primarily composed of quartz. What property of quartz would assist you in identifying these samples?

Figure 10 Hand samples of common sedimentary rocks.

28. Samples G–L all contain calcite. What property of calcite would assist you in identifying these samples?

29. Compare and contrast Sample I (fossiliferous limestone) and Sample J (coquina).

30. Sample G (crystalline limestone) in Figure 10 and Sample A in Figure 6 are both crystalline. How do these samples differ in appearance?

31. What characteristic do Sample Q (agate) and Sample L (travertine) share?

32. Which of these terms most accurately describes the texture of Sample N—*clastic* or *nonclastic*?

33. Sample H is a microcrystalline rock composed of calcite, and Sample O is a microcrystalline rock composed of quartz. What test(s) could you use to figure out which is which?

34. What mineral does Sample D contain that gives it a pinkish color?

Identifying Sedimentary Rocks

The *Sedimentary Rock Identification Key* in Figure 11 divides sedimentary rocks into two groups—detrital and chemical. The primary subdivisions for detrital

SEDIMENTARY ROCK IDENTIFICATION KEY

Detrital Sedimentary Rocks			Chemical Sedimentary Rocks		
Clastic Texture (particle size)	Distinctive Properties	Rock Name	Composition	Distinctive Properties	Rock Name
Gravel Coarse (over 2 mm)	Rounded rock or mineral fragments, typically poorly sorted	Conglomerate	Calcite, CaCO₃ (effervesces in HCl)	Fine to coarse crystalline	Crystalline Limestone
	Angular rock or mineral fragments, typically poorly sorted	Breccia		No visible grains, may exhibit conchoidal fracture	Micrite
Sand Medium (1/16 to 2 mm)	Quartz grains, typically rounded, well sorted	Quartz Sandstone		Visible shells and shell fragments loosely cemented	Coquina
	At least 25% feldspar, typically poorly sorted, angular fragments	Arkose		Various size shells and shell fragments, well cemented	Fossiliferous Limestone
	Mixture of sand and mud, typically poorly sorted	Graywacke		Microscopic shells and clay, soft	Chalk
Silt/mud Fine (1/16 to 1/256 mm)	Mostly silt-size quartz and clay, blocky, gritty	Siltstone		Faint layering, may contain cavities or pores	Travertine
Clay/mud Very fine (less than 1/256 mm)	Mostly clay, splits into layers, may contain fossils	Shale	Quartz, SiO₂	Microcrystalline, may exhibit conchoidal fracture, will scratch glass	Chert (light colored)
	Mostly clay, crumbles easily	Claystone			Flint (dark colored)
					Agate (banded)
			Gypsum CaSO₄•2H₂O	Fine to coarse crystalline, soft	Rock Gypsum
			Halite, NaCl	Fine to coarse crystalline, tastes salty	Rock Salt
			Altered plant fragments	Black brittle organic rock, may be layered	Bituminous Coal

Figure 11 Sedimentary rock identification key.

rocks are based upon grain size, whereas composition is used to subdivide the chemical sedimentary rocks.

35. Place each of the sedimentary rocks supplied by your instructor on a numbered piece of paper. Then complete the *Sedimentary Rock Chart* in Figure 12 for each rock. Use the Sedimentary Rock Identification Key (Figure 11) to determine each specimen's name.

Sedimentary Environments

Sedimentary rocks are extremely important in the study of Earth history. The texture and mineral composition of sedimentary rocks often suggest something about the location (environment) where the sediment accumulated. For example, rock salt forms in warm, shallow seas, where the loss of water by evaporation exceeds the annual rainfall. In addition, fossils and sedimentary structures provide important clues about a rock's history. Think of each sedimentary rock as representing a "place" on Earth where sediment was deposited and later lithified.

Figure 13 illustrates and describes a few modern environments (places) where sediment accumulates.

SEDIMENTARY ROCK CHART

Specimen Number	Texture and Grain Size	Composition or Sediment Name	Detrital or Chemical (Biochemical)	Rock Name

Figure 12 Sedimentary rock chart.

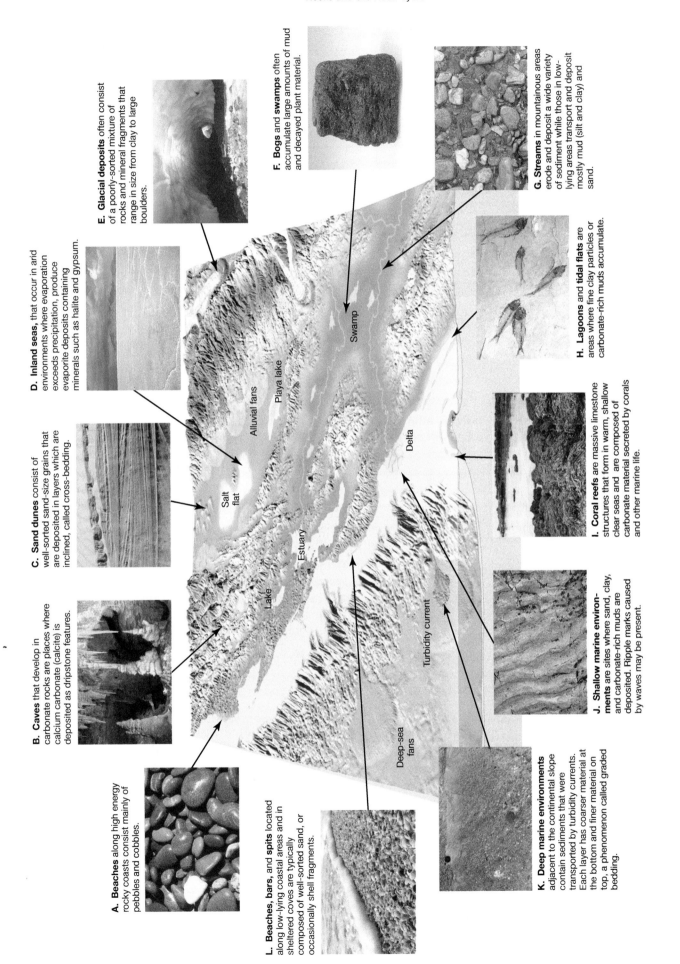

E. Glacial deposits often consist of a poorly-sorted mixture of rocks and mineral fragments that range in size from clay to large boulders.

D. Inland seas, that occur in arid environments where evaporation exceeds precipitation, produce evaporite deposits containing minerals such as halite and gypsum.

C. Sand dunes consist of well-sorted sand-size grains that are deposited in layers which are inclined, called cross-bedding.

B. Caves that develop in carbonate rocks are places where calcium carbonate (calcite) is deposited as dripstone features.

A. Beaches along high energy rocky coasts consist mainly of pebbles and cobbles.

F. Bogs and **swamps** often accumulate large amounts of mud and decayed plant material.

G. Streams in mountainous areas erode and deposit a wide variety of sediment while those in low-lying areas transport and deposit mostly mud (silt and clay) and sand.

H. Lagoons and **tidal flats** are areas where fine clay particles or carbonate-rich muds accumulate.

I. Coral reefs are massive limestone structures that form in warm, shallow clear seas and are composed of carbonate material secreted by corals and other marine life.

J. Shallow marine environments are sites where sand, clay, and carbonate-rich muds are deposited. Ripple marks caused by waves may be present.

K. Deep marine environments adjacent to the continental slope contain sediments that were transported by turbidity currents. Each layer has coarser material at the bottom and finer material on top, a phenomenon called graded bedding.

L. Beaches, bars, and **spits** located along low-lying coastal areas and in sheltered coves are typically composed of well-sorted sand, or occasionally shell fragments.

Alluvial fans

Playa lake

Salt flat

Lake

Estuary

Swamp

Delta

Turbidity current

Deep-sea fans

Figure 13 Sedimentary environments. (Photo C by John S. Shelton; Photo G by Michael Collier; Photo K by Marli Miller; Photo L by David R. Frazier Photolibrary, Inc./Alamy

Figure 14 The orange and yellow cliffs of Utah's Zion National Park.

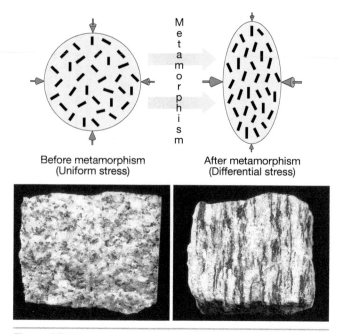

Figure 15 Under directed pressure, linear or platy minerals, such as the micas, become reoriented or recrystallized so that their surfaces are aligned at right angles to the stress. The resulting planar orientation of mineral grains is called foliation.

36. Use Figure 13 to identify the environment(s) (A–L) where the sediment for the following sedimentary rocks could have been deposited.

    Rock gypsum: _____

    Conglomerate: _____

    Sandstone: _____

    Shale: _____

    Bituminous coal: _____

    Travertine: _____

37. Briefly describe the environment that is conducive to the formation of coral reefs.

    _____

38. The rocks in Zion National Park, Utah, consist of layers of well-sorted quartz sandstone shown in Figure 14. Describe the environment that existed when these sediments were deposited. (Hint: Examine the sedimentary environments shown in Figure 13.)

    _____

Metamorphic Rocks

Extensive areas of metamorphic rocks are exposed on every continent in the relatively flat regions known as *shields*. They are also located in the cores of mountains and buried beneath sedimentary rocks on the continents.

Metamorphic Textures

During metamorphism, new minerals often form and/or existing minerals grow larger as the intensity of metamorphism increases. Frequently, mineral crystals that are elongated (such as hornblende) or have a sheet structure (for example, the micas—biotite and muscovite) become oriented perpendicular to compressional forces. The resulting parallel, linear alignment of mineral crystals is called **foliation** (Figure 15). Foliation is associated with many metamorphic rocks and gives them a layered or banded appearance.

Foliated Metamorphic Rocks The mineral crystals in foliated metamorphic rocks are either elongated or have thin, platy shapes and are arranged in a parallel or layered manner. During metamorphism, increased heat and pressure can cause mineral crystals to *become larger* and *foliation to become more obvious*. The various types of foliation, shown in Figure 16A–D, are described below:

Slaty or rock cleavage refers to closely spaced, flat surfaces along which rocks split into thin slabs when struck with a hammer (Figure 16A).
Phyllite texture develops when minute mica crystals in slate begin to increase in size. Phyllite surfaces

FOLIATED TEXTURES

Slate
A. Slaty or rock cleavage

Phyllite
B. Phyllite texture

Mica Schist
C. Schisosity

Gneiss
D. Gneissic texture

NONFOLIATED TEXTURES

Marble
E. Coarse grained

Quartzite
F. Fine grained

Figure 16 Metamorphic textures.

have a shiny, somewhat metallic sheen and often have a wavy surface (Figure 16B).

Schisosity can be identified by a scaly layering of glittery, platy minerals (mainly micas) that are often found in association with deformed quartz and feldspar grains (Figure 16C).

Gneissic texture forms during high-grade metamorphism when ion migration results in the segregation of light and dark minerals (Figure 16D).

Nonfoliated Metamorphic Rocks Nonfoliated metamorphic rocks consist of intergrown crystals of various size and are most often identified by determining their mineral composition (Figure 16E,F). The minerals that comprise them are most often quartz or calcite. Therefore, the hardness test and/or the acid test can be used.

Other Distinguishing Features Some metamorphic rocks have stretched or deformed pebbles or fossils

(Figure 17A). Others contain unusually large crystals called *porphyroblasts* that are surrounded by a fine-grained matrix of other minerals (Figure 17B). These large crystals tend to be minerals that are mainly associated with metamorphic rocks, including garnet, staurolite, and andalusite. Another distinguishing characteristic of some highly deformed metamorphic rocks is that their foliation becomes contorted, as shown in Figure 17C.

Metamorphic Rock Identification

Metamorphic rocks are classified according to their texture and mineral composition. To identify metamorphic rocks, use the *Metamorphic Rock Identification Key* (Figure 18) and follow these steps:

Step 1: Determine whether the rock is foliated or nonfoliated.

Step 2: Determine the size of the mineral grains.

Step 3: If possible, determine the rock's mineral composition and note any other distinctive features.

Step 4: Use the information collected and the Metamorphic Rock Identification Key to determine the name of the rock. The names of the medium- and coarse-grained rocks are often modified with the mineral composition placed in front of the name (for example, *mica schist*).

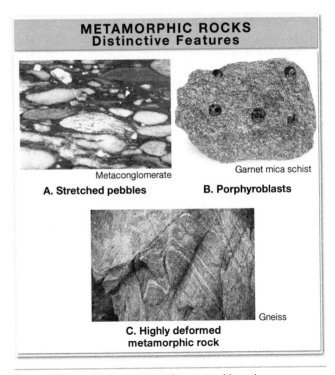

METAMORPHIC ROCKS
Distinctive Features

Metaconglomerate
A. Stretched pebbles

Garnet mica schist
B. Porphyroblasts

Gneiss
C. Highly deformed metamorphic rock

Figure 17 Distinctive features of metamorphic rocks.

METAMORPHIC ROCK IDENTIFICATION KEY

Distinctive Properties	Texture	Grain Size	Rock Name		Parent Rock
Excellent rock cleavage, smooth dull surfaces	Foliated	 Very fine	Slate	Increasing Metamorphism	Shale, or siltstone
Breaks along wavy surfaces, glossy sheen	Foliated	 Fine	Phyllite		Shale, slate, or siltstone
Micas dominate, breaks along scaly foliation	Foliated	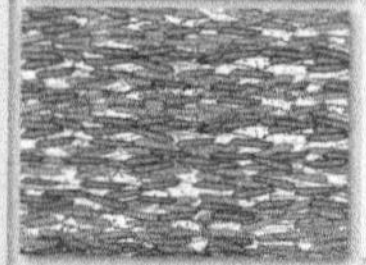 Medium to Coarse	Schist Mica schist Chlorite schist Talc schist Garnet mica schist		Shale, slate, phyllite, or siltstone
Compositional banding due to segregation of dark and light minerals	Foliated	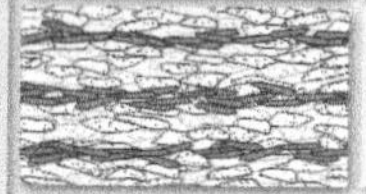 Medium to Coarse	Gneiss		Shale, schist, granite, or volcanic rocks
Banded, deformed rock with zones of light and dark colored crystalline minerals	Foliated	 Medium to Coarse	Migmatite		Shale, granite, or volcanic rocks
Interlocking calcite or dolomite crystals nearly the same size, soft, reacts to HCl	Nonfoliated	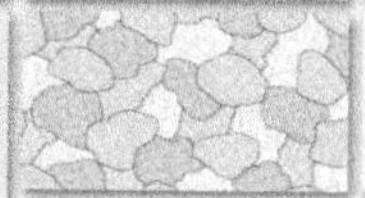 Medium to coarse	Marble		Limestone, dolostone
Fused quartz grains, massive, very hard	Nonfoliated	 Medium to coarse	Quartzite		Quartz sandstone
Round or stretched pebbles that have a preferred orientation	Nonfoliated	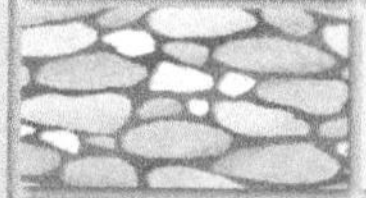 Coarse-grained	Metaconglomerate		Quartz-rich conglomerate
Shiny black rock that may exhibit conchoidal fracture	Nonfoliated	Fine	Anthracite		Bituminous coal
Usually, dark massive rock with dull luster	Nonfoliated	Fine	Hornfels		Any rock type
Very fine grained, typically dull with a greenish color, may contain asbestos fibers	Nonfoliated	Fine	Serpentinite		Basalt or ultramafic rocks
Broken fragments in a haphazard arrangement	Nonfoliated	 Medium to very coarse	Fault breccia		Any rock type

Figure 18 Metamorphic rock identification key.

39. Place each of the metamorphic rocks supplied by your instructor on a numbered piece of paper. Then complete the *Metamorphic Rock Chart* for each rock (Figure 19). Use the Metamorphic Rock Identification Key to determine each specimen's name (Figure 18).

METAMORPHIC ROCK CHART

Sample Number	Foliated or Nonfoliated	Grain Size	Mineral Composition (if identifiable)	Rock Name

Figure 19 Metamorphic rock chart.

Companion Website

The companion website provides numerous opportunities to explore and reinforce the topics of this lab exercise. To access this useful tool, follow these steps:

1. Go to www.mygeoscienceplace.com.
2. Click on "Books Available" at the top of the page.
3. Click on the cover of *Applications and Investigations in Earth Science, 7e*.
4. Select the chapter you want to access. Options are listed in the left column ("Introduction," "Web-based Activities," "Related Websites," and "Field Trips").

Notes and calculations.

Rocks and the Rock Cycle

Name _____   Course/Section _____

Date _____   Due Date _____

1. The rock samples you encountered while completing this exercise are called *hand samples* because you can pick them up in your hand and study them. You can also easily examine hand samples with a hand lens, test them for hardness and reactivity to HCl, and feel and heft them. However, some characteristics of each rock group are so diagnostic that you can observe them at a distance and classify the rocks as igneous, sedimentary, or metamorphic. Examine the rock outcrops shown in Figure 20 and indicate whether each is igneous, sedimentary, or metamorphic.

   Outcrop A: _____

   Outcrop B: _____

   Outcrop C: _____

2. Match each of the metamorphic rocks listed below with one possible parent rock from the following list: bituminous coal, shale, limestone, slate, granite, sandstone.

METAMORPHIC ROCK	NAME OF PARENT ROCK
Marble:	_____
Slate:	_____
Phyllite:	_____
Gneiss:	_____
Quartzite:	_____
Anthracite:	_____

3. Match each term or characteristic with the appropriate rock group.

   A. Foliated texture   **B.** Clastic texture

   C. Gneissic texture   **D.** Chemical rocks

   E. Porphyritic texture   **F.** Lithification

Outcrop A

Outcrop B

Outcrop C

Figure 20   Photos to accompany question 1.

37

G. Alignment of mineral grains

H. Silt-size particles

I. Vesicular texture

J. Strata or beds

K. Feslic composition

L. Slaty texture

M. Glassy texture

N. Evaporite deposits

O. Detrital rocks

Igneous rocks: _____

Sedimentary rocks: _____

Metamorphic rocks: _____

4. Name the foliated metamorphic rocks shown in Figure 21 and list their names in order from lowest to highest metamorphic grade.

5. Name each of the rocks shown in Figure 22 and name the rock group to which each belongs.

A. _____   **B.** _____
(Name)   (Name)

_____   _____
(Rock Group)   (Rock Group)

C. _____   **D.** _____
(Name)   (Name)

_____   _____
(Rock Group)   (Rock Group)

E. _____   **F.** _____
(Name)   (Name)

_____   _____
(Rock Group)   (Rock Group)

_____   _____
(Name)    (Name)

_____   _____
(Name)    (Name)

Lowest _____

_____

_____

Highest _____

Figure 21 Photos to accompany question 4.

G. _____   **H.** _____
(Name)   (Name)

Figure 22 Photos to accompany question 5.

Dating of Rocks, Fossils, and Geologic Events

•CONTRIBUTING AUTHORS•

Jonathan Bushee • *Northern Kentucky University*

John K. Osmond • *Florida State University*

Raman J. Singh • *Northern Kentucky University*

OBJECTIVES

A. Learn and be able to apply techniques for relative age dating of Earth materials and events.

B. Use fossils to date some rock bodies and infer some of Earth's history.

C. Learn and be able to apply techniques for absolute age dating of Earth materials and events.

D. Be able to apply relative and absolute dating techniques to analyze two field sites and infer their geologic history.

E. Be able to apply relative dating techniques to analyze logs of five wells and correlate among them.

MATERIALS

Pencil, eraser, laboratory notebook, calculator, and colored pencils (optional) plus a ruler and protractor cut from the GeoTools Sheet.

INTRODUCTION

If you could dig a hole deep into Earth's crust, then you would encounter the **geologic record,** layers of rock stacked one atop the other like pages in a book. As each new layer of sediment or rock forms today, it cov-ers the older layers of the geologic record beneath it and becomes the youngest layer of the geologic record. Thus, rock layers form a *sequence* from oldest at the bottom to youngest at the top. They also have different colors, textures, chemical compositions, and **fossils** (any evidence of ancient life) depending on the environmental conditions under which they were formed. Geologists have studied sequences of rock layers wherever they are exposed in mines, quarries, river beds, road cuts, wells, and mountain sides throughout the world. They have also *correlated* the layers (traced them from one place to another) across regions and continents. Thus, the geologic record of rock layers is essentially a stack of stone pages in a giant natural book of Earth history. And like the pages in any old book, the rock layers have been folded, fractured (cracked), torn (faulted), and even removed by geologic events.

Geologists tell time based on relative and absolute dating techniques. **Relative age dating** is the process of determining when something formed or happened in relation to other things. For example, if you have a younger brother and an older sister, then you could describe your relative age by saying that you are younger than your sister and older than your brother. **Absolute age dating** is the process of determining when something formed or happened in exact units of time such as days, months, or years. Using the example above, you could describe your absolute age just by saying how old you are in years.

Geologists "read" and infer Earth history from rocky outcrops and geologic cross sections by

From *Laboratory Manual in Physical Geology*, Eighth Edition, American Geological Institute, National Association of Geoscience Teachers, Richard M. Busch, Dennis Tasa. Copyright © 2009 by American Geological Institute. Published by Pearson Prentice Hall. All rights reserved.

observing rock layers, recognizing geologic structures, and evaluating age relationships among the layers and structures. The so-called *geologic time scale* is a chart of named intervals of the geologic record and their ages in both relative and absolute time. It has taken thousands of geoscientists, from all parts of the world, more than a century to construct the present form of the geologic time scale.

Just as authors organize books according to sections, chapters, and pages, geologists have subdivided the rock layers of the geologic record into named eonothems (the largest units), erathems, systems, series, stages, and zones of rock on the basis of fossils, minerals, and other historical features they contained. These physical divisions of rock also represent specific intervals of geologic time. An *eonothem* of rock represents an eon of time, an *erathem* of rock represents an era of time, a *system* of rock represents a period of time, and so on in the table below.

ROCK UNITS

(Division of the Geologic Record)	CORRESPONDING GEOLOGIC TIME UNITS
Eonothem (largest)	Eon of time (longest unit)
Erathem	Era of time
System	Period of time
Series	Epoch of time
Stage	Age of time
Zone	Chron of time

PART A: DETERMINING RELATIVE AGES OF ROCKS BASED ON THEIR PHYSICAL RELATIONSHIPS

A geologist's initial challenge in the field is to subdivide the local sequence of sediments and bodies of rock into mappable units that can be correlated from one site to the next. Subdivision is based on color, texture, rock type, or other physical features of the rocks, and the mappable units are called **formations.** Formations can be subdivided into *members,* or even individual strata. Surfaces between any of these kinds of units are *contacts.*

Geologists use six basic laws for determining relative age relationships among bodies of rock based on their physical relationships. They are:

- **Law of Original Horizontality**—*Sedimentary layers (***strata***) and lava flows were originally deposited as relatively horizontal sheets, like a layer cake. If they are no longer horizontal or flat, it is because they*

have been displaced by subsequent movements of the Earth's crust.

- **Law of Lateral Continuity**—*Lava flows and strata extend laterally in all directions until they thin to nothing (pinch out) or reach the edge of their basin of deposition.*

- **Law of Superposition**—*In an undisturbed sequence of strata or lava flows, the oldest layer is at the bottom of the sequence and the youngest is at the top.*

- **Law of Inclusions**—*Any piece of rock (clast) that has become included in another rock or body of sediment must be older than the rock or sediment into which it has been incorporated.* Such a clast (usually a rock fragment, crystal, or fossil) is called an **inclusion.** The surrounding body of rock is called the **matrix** (or groundmass). Thus, an inclusion is older than its surrounding matrix.

- **Law of Cross-Cutting**—*Any feature that cuts across a rock or body of sediment must be younger than the rock or sediment that it cuts across.* Such crosscutting features include fractures (cracks in rock), faults (fractures along which movement has occurred), or masses of magma (*igneous intrusions*) that cut across preexisting rocks before they cooled. When a body of magma intrudes preexisting rocks, a narrow *zone of contact metamorphism* usually forms in the preexisting rocks adjacent to the intrusion.

- **Law of Unconformities**—*Surfaces called unconformities represent gaps in the geologic record that formed wherever layers were not deposited for a time or else layers were removed by erosion.* Most contacts between adjacent strata or formations are conformities, meaning that rocks on both sides of them formed at about the same time. An unconformity is a rock surface that represents a gap in the geologic record. It is like the place where pages are missing from a book. An unconformity can be a buried surface where there was a pause in sedimentation, a time between two lava flows, or a surface that was eroded before more sediment was deposited on top of it.

There are three kinds of unconformities (Figure 1). A **disconformity** is an unconformity between *parallel* strata or lava flows. Most disconformities are very irregular surfaces, and pieces of the underlying rock are often included in the strata above them. An **angular unconformity** is an unconformity between two sets of strata that are not parallel to one another. It forms when new horizontal layers cover up older layers folded by mountain-building processes and eroded down to a nearly level surface. A **nonconformity** is an

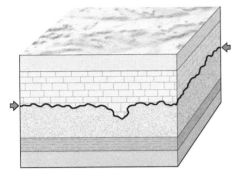
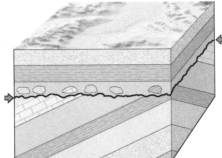
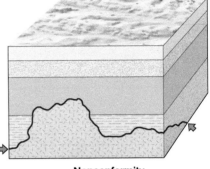

Disconformity

In a succession of rock layers (sedimentary strata or lava flows) parallel to one another, the disconformity surface is a gap in the layering. The gap may be a non-depositional surface where some layers never formed for a while, or the gap may be an erosional surface where some layers were removed before younger layers covered up the surface.

Angular unconformity

An angular unconformity is an erosional surface between two bodies of layered sedimentary strata or lava flows that are not parallel. The gap is because the older body of layered rock was tilted and partly eroded (rock was removed) before a younger body of horizontal rock layers covered the eroded surface.

Nonconformity

A nonconformity is an erosional surface between older igneous and/or metamorphic rocks and younger rock layers (sedimentary strata or lava flows). The gap is because some of the older igneous and/or metamorphic rocks were partly eroded (rock was removed) before the younger rock layers covered the eroded surface.

FIGURE 1 Three kinds of unconformities—surfaces that represent gaps (missing layers) in the geologic record; analogous to a gap (place where pages are missing) in a book. Red arrows point to the unconformity surface (bold black line) in each block diagram.

unconformity between younger sedimentary rocks and subjacent metamorphic or igneous rocks. It forms when stratified sedimentary rocks or lava flows are deposited on eroded igneous or metamorphic rocks.

Analyze and evaluate Figures 2–8 to learn how the above laws of relative age dating are applied in cross sections of Earth's crust. These are the kinds of two-dimensional cross sections of Earth's crust that are exposed in road cuts, quarry walls, and mountain sides. *Ignore the symbols for fossils until Part B. Be sure that you consider all of these examples before proceeding.*

Questions

1. Refer to the geologic cross sections in Figures 9 and 10. The colors and symbols for rock types, contacts, faults, unconformities, and zones of contact metamorphism are the same as the symbols used in Figure 4. For each figure, determine the relative ages of rock units and other features labeled with letters. Indicate the sequence in which the labeled features developed by writing the letters from oldest (first) to youngest (latest) in the blanks provided. Refer back to Figures 1–8 and the laws of relative age dating based on physical relationships, as needed.

2. Refer to Figure 10, which is a cross section of the inner gorge of Grand Canyon, Arizona. Notice the names and relative ages of the formations

(named rock units). Based on your determination of the relative age relationships of these formations (which you listed from oldest to youngest, by letter, in Question 1) and associated other features (unconformities, zones of contact metamorphism), write three paragraphs about the Grand Canyon.

a. In the first paragraph, use names and rock types of the formations to describe events that occurred in the region during Precambrian time.

b. In the second paragraph, use names and rock types of the formations to describe events that occurred in the region during the Cambrian Period of time.

c. In the third paragraph, describe what geologic events are occurring at the present time and infer what and where different kinds of unconformities (disconformity, angular unconformity, nonconformity) are forming.

3. Refer to the geologic cross sections in Figures 11 and 12. For each figure, determine the relative ages of rock units and other features labeled with letters. Indicate the sequence in which the labeled features developed by writing the letters from oldest (first) to youngest (latest) in the blanks provided. Refer back to Figures 1–8 and the laws of relative age dating based on physical relationships, as needed. *More than one solution is possible for both of these figures so be prepared to justify your reasoning if asked to do so.*

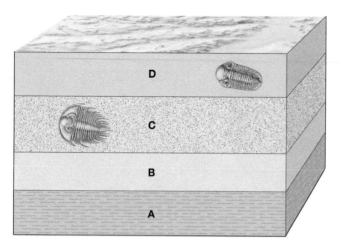

FIGURE 2 This is a sequence of strata that has maintained its original horizontality and does not seem to be disturbed. Therefore, Formation **A** is the oldest, because it is on the bottom of a sedimentary sequence of rocks. **D** is the youngest, because it is at the top of the sedimentary sequence. The sequence of events was deposition of **A**, **B**, **C**, and **D**, in that order and stacked one atop the other.

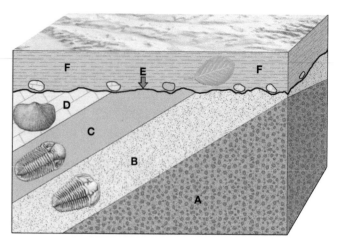

FIGURE 3 This is another sequence of strata, some of which do not have their original horizontality. Formation **A** is the oldest, because it is at the bottom of the sedimentary sequence. Formation **F** is youngest, because it forms the top of that sequence. Tilting and erosion of the sequence occurred after **D** but before deposition of Formation **F**. **E** is an angular unconformity.

The sequence of events began with deposition of **A**, **B**, **C**, and **D** in that order and stacked one atop the other. The sequence was then tilted, and its top was eroded. Siltstone **F** was deposited horizontally on top of the erosional surface, which is now an angular unconformity.

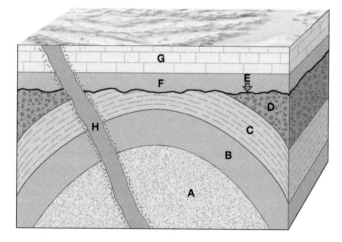

FIGURE 4 The body of igneous rock **H** is the youngest rock unit, because it cuts across all of the others. (When a narrow body of igneous rock cuts across strata in this way, it is called a **dike**.) **A** is the oldest formation, because it is at the bottom of the sedimentary rock sequence that is cut by **H**. Folding and erosion occurred after **D** was deposited, but before **F** was deposited. **E** is an angular unconformity.

The sequence of events began with deposition of formations **A** through **D** in alphabetical order and one atop the other. The sequence was folded, and the top of the fold was eroded. Formation **F** was deposited horizontally atop the folded sequence and the erosional surface, which became angular unconformity **E**. **G** was deposited atop **F**. Lastly, a magma intruded across all of the strata and cooled to form basalt dike **H**.

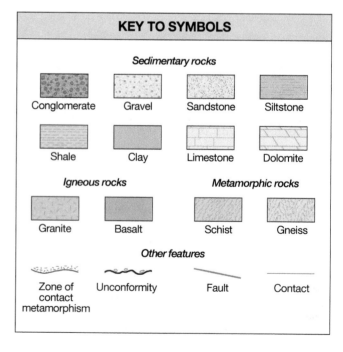

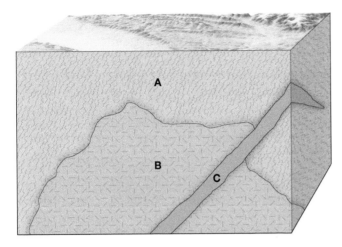

FIGURE 5 The body of granite **B** must have formed from the cooling of a body of magma that intruded the preexisting rock **A**, called **country rock.** The country rock is schist **A** containing a zone of contact metamorphism adjacent to the granite. Therefore, the sequence of events began with a body of country rock **A**. The country rock was intruded by a body of magma, which caused development of a zone of contact metamorphism and cooled to form granite **B**. Lastly, another body of magma intruded across both **A** and **B**. It caused development of a second zone of contact metamorphism and cooled to form basalt dike **C**.

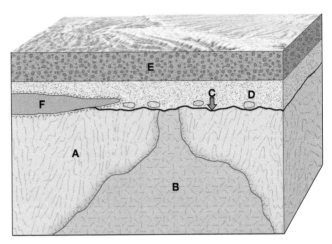

FIGURE 6 At the base of this rock sequence there is gneiss **A**, which is separated from granite **B** by a zone of contact metamorphism. This suggests that a body of magma intruded **A**, then cooled to form the contact zone and granite **B**. There must have been erosion of both **A** and **B** *after* this intrusion (to form surface **C**), because there is no contact metamorphism between **B** and **D**. Formation **D** was deposited horizontally atop the eroded igneous and metamorphic rocks, forming nonconformity **C**. Sometime after **D** was deposited (before or after deposition of **E**), a second body of magma **F** intruded across **A**, **C**, and **D**. Such an intrusive igneous body that is intruded along (parallel to) the strata is called a **sill** (**F**).

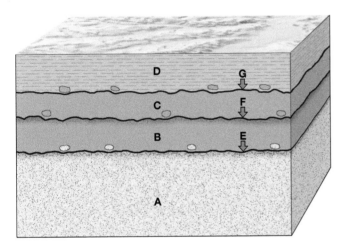

FIGURE 7 Notice that this is a sequence of strata and basalt lava flows (that have cooled to form the basalt). There are zones of contact metamorphism beneath both of the basalt lava flows. The sequence of events must have begun with deposition of sandstone **A**, because it is on the bottom. A lava flow was deposited atop **A** and cooled to form basalt **B**. This first lava flow caused development of the zone of contact metamorphism in **A** and the development of disconformity **E**. A second lava flow was deposited atop **B** and cooled to form basalt **C**. This lava flow caused the development of a zone of contact metamorphism and a disconformity at the top of **B**. An erosional surface developed atop **C**, and the surface became a disconformity **G** when shale **D** was deposited on top of it.

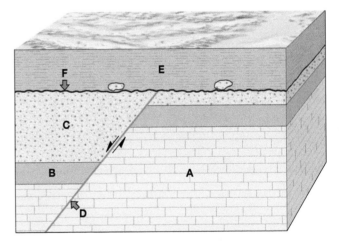

FIGURE 8 This is a sequence of relatively horizontal strata: **A**, **B**, **C**, and **E**. **A** must be the oldest of these formations, because it is on the bottom. **E** is the youngest of these formations, because it is on top. Formations **A**, **B**, and **C** are cut by a fault, which does not cut **E**. This means that the fault **D** must be younger than **C** and older than **E**. **F** is a disconformity. The sequence of events began with deposition of formations **A**, **B**, and **C**, in that order and one atop the other. This sequence was then cut by fault **D**. After faulting, the land surface was eroded. When siltstone **E** was deposited on the erosional surface, it became disconformity **F**.

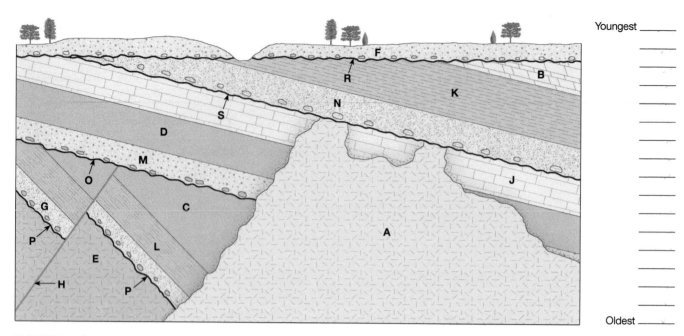

Youngest _____

_____
_____
_____
_____
_____
_____
_____
_____
_____
_____
_____
_____
_____
_____
_____
_____
_____

Oldest _____

FIGURE 9 Geologic cross section for relative age analysis. Place letters on the lines along the right side of the cross section to indicate the relative ages of the rock units and other features (unconformities, fault), from oldest (first) to youngest (last).

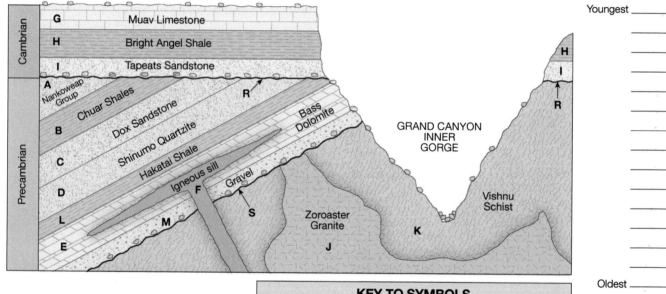

Youngest _____

_____
_____
_____
_____
_____
_____
_____
_____
_____
_____
_____
_____

Oldest _____

KEY TO SYMBOLS

Sedimentary rocks

Conglomerate   Gravel   Sandstone   Siltstone

Shale   Clay   Limestone   Dolomite

Igneous rocks   *Metamorphic rocks*

Granite   Basalt   Schist   Gneiss

Other features

Zone of contact metamorphism   Unconformity   Fault   Contact

FIGURE 10 Geologic cross section of the Grand Canyon for relative age analysis. Place letters on the lines along the right side of the cross section to indicate the relative ages of the rock units and unconformities, from oldest (first) to youngest (last).

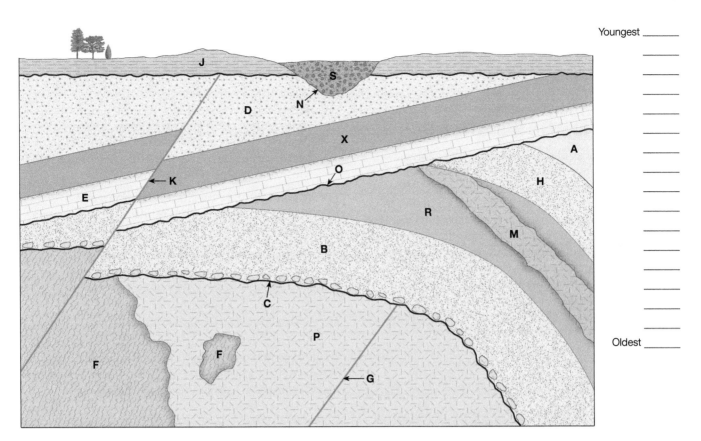

FIGURE 11 Geologic cross section for relative age analysis. Place letters on the lines along the right side of the cross section to indicate the relative ages of the rock units and other features (unconformities, faults), from oldest (first) to youngest (last).

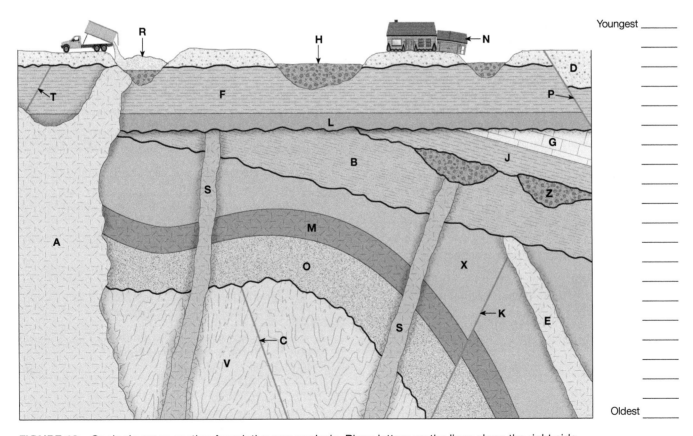

FIGURE 12 Geologic cross section for relative age analysis. Place letters on the lines along the right side of the cross section to indicate the relative ages of the rock units and other features (unconformities, faults), from oldest (first) to youngest (last).

PART B: USING FOSSILS TO DETERMINE AGE RELATIONSHIPS

The sequence of strata that makes up the geologic record is a graveyard filled with the fossils of millions of kinds of organisms that are now extinct. Geologists know that they existed only on the basis of their fossilized remains or the traces of their activities (like tracks and trails). Geologists have also determined that fossil organisms originate, co-exist, or disappear from the geologic record in a definite sequential order recognized throughout the world, so *any rock layer containing a group of fossils can be identified and dated in relation to other layers on the basis of its fossils.* This is known as the **Principle of Fossil Succession.**

The sequence of strata in which fossils of a particular organism are found is called a **range zone,** which represents a chron of time. Organisms whose range zones have been used to represent named divisions of the geologic time scale are called **index fossils.**

The range zones of some well-known Phanerozoic index fossils are presented on the right side of Figure 13. Relative ages of the rocks containing these fossils are presented as *periods* and *eras* on the left side of Figure 13. By noting the range zone of a fossil (vertical black line), you can determine the corresponding era(s) or period(s) of time in which it lived. For example, the fossil record indicates that sharks have lived from (and are an index fossil for) late in the Devonian Period of the Paleozoic Era to the present time. All of the different species of dinosaurs lived and died during the Mesozoic Era of time, long before (many layers below) the time when humans first existed and left a record of fossils. Notice that Figure 13 also includes the following groups:

- **Brachiopods** (pink on chart): marine invertebrate animals with two symmetrical seashells of unequal size. They range throughout the Paleozoic, Mesozoic, and Cenozoic Eras, but they were most abundant in the Paleozoic Era. Only a few species exist today, so they are nearly extinct.

- **Trilobites** (orange on chart): an extinct group of marine invertebrate animals related to lobsters. They are only found in Paleozoic rocks, so they are a good index fossil for the Paleozoic Era and its named subdivisions.

- **Plants** (dark green on chart)

- **Reptiles** (pale green on chart): the group of vertebrate animals that includes lizards, snakes, turtles, and dinosaurs. **Dinosaurs** are only found in Mesozoic rocks, so they are an index fossil for the Mesozoic and its subdivisions.

- **Mammals** (gray on chart): the group of vertebrate animals (including humans) that are warm blooded, nurse their young, and have hair.

- **Amphibians** (brown on chart): the group of vertebrate animals that includes frogs and salamanders.

- **Sharks** (blue on chart).

Notice that absolute ages in millions of years are also presented on Figure 13. Determining absolute ages will be addressed in Part C, but you will need to use the absolute ages in this figure to answer some of the questions below.

Questions

4. Analyze the fossiliferous rock in Figure 14.

    a. Based on Figure 13, what is the *relative age* of the rock in Figure 14? Explain your reasoning.

    b. Based on Figure 13, what is the *absolute age* of the rock in Figure 14? Explain your reasoning.

5. Analyze the fossiliferous rock in Figure 15.

    a. Based on Figure 13, what is the *relative age* of the rock in Figure 15? Explain your reasoning.

    b. Based on Figure 13, what is the *absolute age* of the rock in Figure 15? Explain your reasoning.

6. Re-examine the geologic cross section in Figure 2 on the basis of its fossils.

    a. Which one of the contacts between lettered layers is a disconformity?

    b. What is missing at the disconformity?

    c. If the present landscape in this cross section were covered today with a layer of sediment, then how much time would the resulting disconformity represent? Explain your reasoning.

7. What geologic events occurred during the Mesozoic Era in the region where Figure 3 is located? Explain your reasoning.

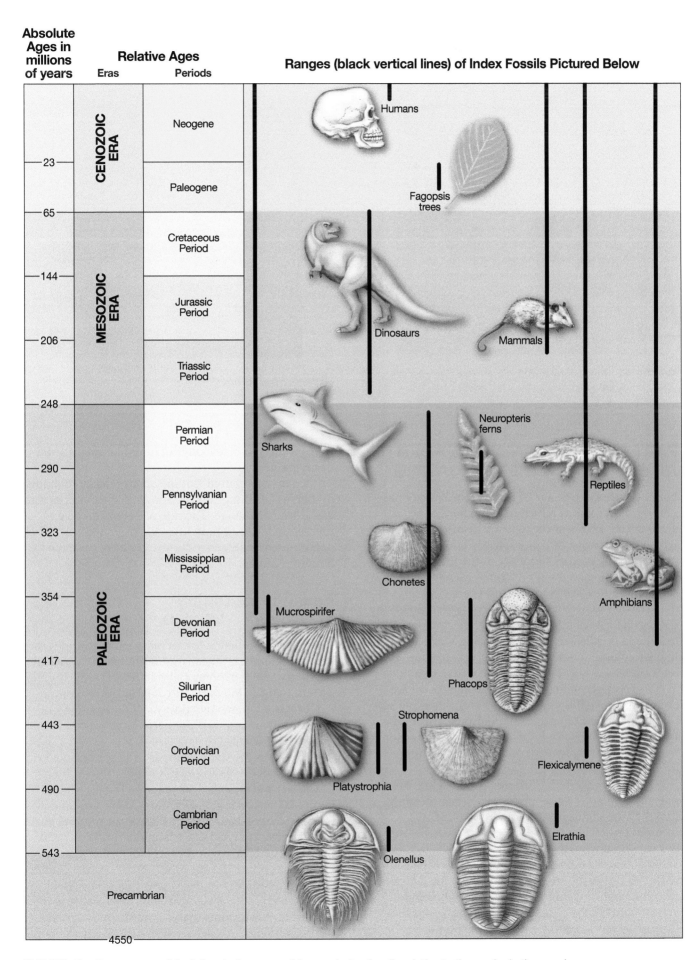

FIGURE 13 Range zones (black lines) of some well-known index fossils relative to the geologic time scale.

FIGURE 14   Fossiliferous rock sample for age analysis.

FIGURE 15   Fossiliferous rock sample for age analysis.

PART C: DETERMINING ABSOLUTE AGES BY RADIOMETRIC DATING

You measure the passage of time on the basis of the rates and rhythms at which regular changes occur around you. For example, you are aware of the rate at which hands move on a clock, the rhythm of day and night, and the regular sequence of the four seasons. These regular changes allow you to measure the passage of minutes, hours, days, and years.

Another way to measure the passage of time is by the regular rate of decay of radioactive isotopes. This technique is called **radiometric dating** and is one way that geologists determine absolute ages of some geologic materials.

You may recall that **isotopes** of an element are atoms that have the same number of protons and electrons but different numbers of neutrons. This means that the different isotopes of an element vary in atomic weight (mass number) but not in atomic number (number of protons).

There are about 350 different isotopes that occur naturally. Some of these are *stable isotopes*, meaning that they are not radioactive and do not decay through time. The others are *radioactive isotopes* that decay spontaneously, at regular rates through time. When a mass of atoms of a radioactive isotope is incorporated into the structure of a newly formed crystal or seashell, it is referred to as a **parent isotope.** When atoms of the parent isotope decay to a stable form, they have become a **daughter isotope.** A parent isotope and its corresponding daughter are called a **decay pair.**

Atoms of a parent isotope always decay to atoms of their stable daughter isotope at an exponential rate that does not change. The rate of decay can be expressed in terms of **half-life**—the time it takes for half of the parent atoms in a sample to decay to stable daughter atoms.

Radiometric Dating of Geologic Materials

The decay parameters for all radioactive isotopes can be represented graphically as in Figure 16. Notice that the decay rate is exponential (not linear)—during the second half-life interval, only half of the remaining half of parent atoms will decay. All radioactive isotopes decay in this way, but each decay pair has its own value for half-life.

Half-lives for some isotopes used for radiometric dating have been experimentally determined by physicists and chemists, as noted in the top chart of Figure 16. For example, Uranium-238 is a radioactive isotope (parent) found in crystals of the mineral zircon. It decays to Lead-206 (daughter) and has a half-life of about 4,500 million years (4.5 billion years).

To determine the age of an object, it must contain atoms of a radioactive decay pair that originated when the object formed. You must then measure the percent of those atoms that is parent atoms (**P**) and the percent that is daughter atoms (**D**). This is general-

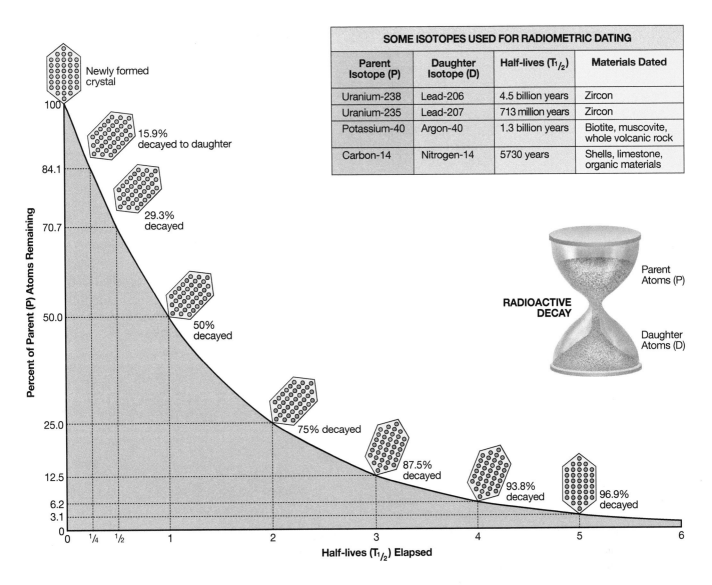

SOME ISOTOPES USED FOR RADIOMETRIC DATING			
Parent Isotope (P)	Daughter Isotope (D)	Half-lives (T$_{1/2}$)	Materials Dated
Uranium-238	Lead-206	4.5 billion years	Zircon
Uranium-235	Lead-207	713 million years	Zircon
Potassium-40	Argon-40	1.3 billion years	Biotite, muscovite, whole volcanic rock
Carbon-14	Nitrogen-14	5730 years	Shells, limestone, organic materials

DECAY PARAMETERS FOR ALL RADIOACTIVE DECAY PAIRS			
Percent of Parent Atoms (P)	Percent of Daughter Atoms (D)	Half-lives Elapsed	Age
100.0	0.0	0	0.000 x T$_{1/2}$
98.9	1.1	1/64	0.015 x T$_{1/2}$
97.9	2.1	1/32	0.031 x T$_{1/2}$
95.8	4.2	1/16	0.062 x T$_{1/2}$
91.7	8.3	1/8	0.125 x T$_{1/2}$
84.1	15.9	1/4	0.250 x T$_{1/2}$
70.7	29.3	1/2	0.500 x T$_{1/2}$
50.0	50.0	1	1.000 x T$_{1/2}$
35.4	64.6	1½	1.500 x T$_{1/2}$
25.0	75.0	2	2.000 x T$_{1/2}$
12.5	87.5	3	3.000 x T$_{1/2}$
6.2	93.8	4	4.000 x T$_{1/2}$
3.1	96.9	5	5.000 x T$_{1/2}$

FIGURE 16 Some isotopes useful for radiometric dating and their decay parameters. The half-life of each decay pair is different (top chart), but the graph and decay parameters (bottom charts) are the same for all decay pairs.

ly done in a chemistry laboratory with an instrument called a *mass spectrometer*. Based on **P** and **D** and the chart at the bottom of Figure 16, find the number of half-lives that have elapsed and the object's corresponding age in number of half-lives. Finally, multiply that number of half-lives by the known half-life for that decay pair (noted in the top chart of Figure 16).

For example, a sample of Precambrian granite contains biotite mineral crystals, so it can be dated using the Potassium-40 to Argon-40 decay pair. If there are 3 Argon-40 atoms in the sample for every 1 Potassium-40 atom, then the sample is 25.0% Potassium-40 parent atoms (**P**) and 75.0% Argon-40 daughter atoms (**D**). This means that 2 half-lives have elapsed, so the age of the biotite (and the granite) is 2.0 times 1.3 billion years, which equals 2.6 billion years.

Questions

8. A solidified lava flow containing zircon mineral crystals is present in a sequence of rock layers that are exposed in a hillside. A mass spectrometer analysis was used to count the atoms of Uranium-235 and Lead-207 isotopes in zircon samples from the lava flow. The analysis revealed that 71% of the atoms were Uranium-235, and 29% of the atoms were Lead-207.

a. About how many half-lives of the Uranium-235 to Lead-207 decay pair have elapsed in the zircon crystals?

b. What is the absolute age of the lava flow based on its zircon crystals? Show your calculations.

c. What is the age of the rock layers beneath the lava flow?

d. What is the age of the rock layers above the lava flow?

9. Astronomers think that the Earth probably formed at the same time as all of the other rocky materials in our solar system, including the oldest meteorites. The oldest meteorites ever found on Earth contain nearly equal amounts of both Uranium-238 and Lead-206. Based on Figure 16, what is Earth's age? Explain your reasoning.

10. If you assume that the global amount of radiocarbon (formed by cosmic-ray bombardment of atoms in the upper atmosphere and then dissolved in rain and seawater) is constant, then decaying Carbon-14 is continuously replaced in

organisms while they are alive. However, when an organism dies, the amount of its Carbon-14 decreases as it decays to Nitrogen-14.

a. The carbon in a buried peat bed has about 6% of the Carbon-14 of modern shells. What is the age of the peat bed? Explain.

b. In sampling the peat bed you must be careful to avoid any young plant roots or old limestone. Why?

11. Layers of sand on a New Jersey beach contain common zircon crystals.

a. Could the zircon crystals be used to date exactly when the layers of sand were deposited? Explain.

b. Suggest a rule that geologists should follow when they date rocks according to radiometric ages of crystals inside the rocks.

PART D: INFER THE GEOLOGIC HISTORY OF TWO FIELD SITES

Questions

12. Refer to Figure 17.

a. What is the relative age of the sedimentary rocks in this rock exposure? Explain.

b. What is the absolute age of the sill? Explain.

c. Locate the fault. How much displacement has occurred along this fault?

d. Explain the geologic history of this region, starting with deposition of the sandstone and ending with the time this picture was taken. Use names of relative ages of geologic time and absolute ages in your explanation. *Assume that the fault occurred after emplacement of the sill.*

13. Carefully examine Figure 18, a surface mine (strip mine) in northeastern Pennsylvania's anthracite coal mining district. Describe the age and all of the events that have happened to the fossil plants from the time when they were alive to the time when they were exposed by bulldozers.
Your reasoning may differ from that of other students, because more than one inference is possible about the geologic history of the site. Be prepared to discuss your reasoning with other members of your class.

FIGURE 17 Surface mine (strip mine) in northern New Mexico, from which bituminous coal is being extracted. Note the sill, sedimentary rocks, fossils, whole-rock data, and fault.

WEST

EAST

Coal

Fossiliferous sandstone

Fossiliferous sandstone

Fossil plants

FIGURE 18 Surface mine (strip mine) in northeastern Pennsylvania, from which anthracite coal was extracted. Close-ups show plant fossils that were found at the site.

PART E: CONSTRUCT AND INTERPRET A SUBSURFACE GEOLOGIC CROSS SECTION

The top of Figure 19 is a cross section of five wells drilled along a west–east line. At the bottom of Figure 19 are well logs for these wells. These logs are a record of the faults and rock units (layers) intersected by each well. The dip (inclination) of faults or any rock units that are no longer horizontal is also noted. You also need to know the lithologic descriptions of the rock units:

Unit 1: Cross-bedded eolian (wind-blown) sandstone

Unit 2: Brown-to-gray siltstone with shale zones and some coal seams

Unit 3: Parallel-bedded, poorly sorted sandstone

Unit 4: Conglomerate

Unit 5: Poorly sorted sandstone with some clay, silt, pebbles

Unit 6: Black, clayey shale

Unit 7: Parallel-bedded, well-sorted, coarse-grained sandstone

Unit 8: Black shale

Unit 9: Gray limestone

Complete the cross section in Figure 19. On each well (vertical lines), mark with ticks the elevations of the contacts between units (lightly in pencil). For example, in well A, unit 1 extends from the surface (2400 feet) to 2100 feet, so make tick marks at these points; unit 2 extends from 2100 to 2050 feet, so make ticks at these points; and so on. Label each unit number lightly beside each column, between the ticks.

Pay careful attention to the *dip* (inclination) *angles* indicated for faults and some rock units that are not horizontal. When you make tick marks, it is very helpful to angle them approximately to indicate dip (use a protractor). This is especially true if you encounter any *faults* in the cross section.

When you have all units plotted in the five wells, connect corresponding points between wells. (You are *correlating* well logs when you do this. You are also preparing a subsurface cross section of the type actually constructed by petroleum-exploration geologists.)

From the lithologic descriptions given, you can fill in some of the rock units with patterns—for example, sandstone (dots), conglomerate (tiny circles), and coal (solid black). Use the symbols given in Figure 4. Then complete the items below.

Questions

14. What is the nature and geologic origin of the bottom contact of Unit 2?

15. Why is coal not found in wells A and B, whereas two coal seams are found in well E?

16. Wells A and E are **dry holes,** so-called because they produced no petroleum. But the others produce petroleum. An oil pool is penetrated in well B from 750 feet to 650 feet, in well C from 550 down to 500 feet, and in well D from 750 down to 500 feet. Sketch and label the outline of the oil pools on the cross section and explain why the oil was trapped there.

17. Why is there no oil in either well A or well E?

18. Using the laws of original horizontality, superposition, and cross-cutting (refer back to part A of this laboratory if necessary), describe the sequence of events that developed this geologic situation.

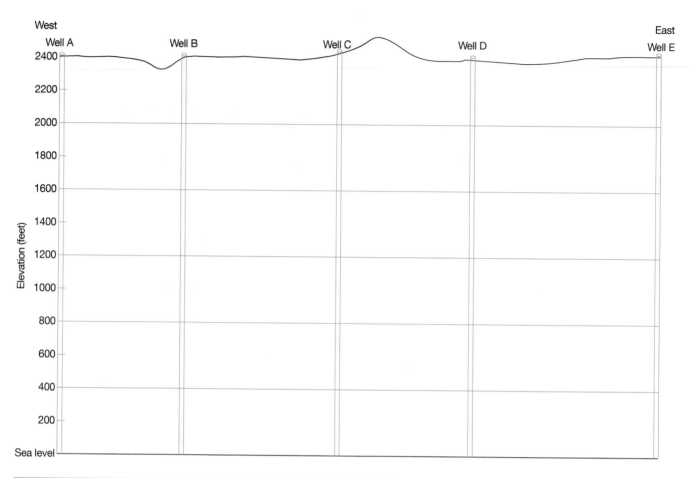

West   East

Well A   Well B   Well C   Well D   Well E

Elevation (feet)

Well A

2400–2100	Unit 1, horizontal
2100–2050	Unit 2, horizontal
2050–1700	Unit 3, dips westward 15°
1700–1150	Unit 4, dips westward 15°
1150– 800	Unit 5, dips westward 15°
800– 550	Unit 6, dips westward 15°
550– 200	Unit 7, dips westward 15°
Bottom of well	

Well B

2300–2100	Unit 1, horizontal
2100–1980	Unit 2, horizontal
1980–1650	Unit 3, dips westward 15°
1650	Fault, dips eastward 60°
1650–1350	Unit 4, dips westward 15°
1350–1000	Unit 5, dips westward 15°
1000– 750	Unit 6, dips westward 15°
750– 200	Unit 7, dips westward 15°
200–sea level	Unit 8, dips westward 15°
Bottom of well	

Well C

2350–2100	Unit 1, horizontal
2100–1900	Unit 2, horizontal; coal seam at 1950
1900–1700	Unit 3, dips westward 15°
1700–1150	Unit 4, dips westward 15°

1150– 800	Unit 5, dips westward 15°
800– 550	Unit 6, dips westward 15°
550– 200	Unit 7, dips westward 15°
200	Fault; dips eastward 60°
200– 100	Unit 9, dips westward 15°
Bottom of well	

Well D

2300–2100	Unit 1, horizontal
2100–1800	Unit 2, horizontal; coal seam at 1950
1800–1350	Unit 4, horizontal
1350–1000	Unit 5, horizontal
1000– 750	Unit 6, horizontal
750– 200	Unit 7, horizontal
200– 100	Unit 8, horizontal
Bottom of well	

Well E

2400–2100	Unit 1, horizontal
2100–1650	Unit 2, horizontal; coal seams at 1950 and 1850
1650–1450	Unit 3, dips eastward 21°
1450– 900	Unit 4, dips eastward 21°
900– 550	Unit 5, dips eastward 21°
550– 300	Unit 6, dips eastward 21°
300– 200	Unit 7, dips eastward 21°
Bottom of well	

FIGURE 19 Cross section of wells and their well logs. Refer to text for descriptions of the rock units.

Topographic Maps, Aerial Photographs, and Satellite Images

·CONTRIBUTING AUTHORS·

Charles G. Higgins • *University of California*

Evelyn M. Vandendolder • *Arizona Geological Survey*

John R. Wagner • *Clemson University*

James R. Wilson • *Weber State College*

OBJECTIVES

A. Be able to locate features on topographic maps using map symbols and colors, latitude and longitude, the U.S. Public Land Survey System (PLS), the Universal Transverse Mercator System (UTM), and compass bearings.

B. Be able to interpret four kinds of map scales (ratio scales, fractional scales, verbal scales, graphic bar scales) and convert one scale to another.

C. Be able to construct topographic maps by drawing contour lines based on points of known elevations for areas of Earth's surface.

D. Be able to interpret contour lines to measure gradients and relief and identify hills, saddles, ridges, spurs, valleys, closed depressions, steep slopes, gentle slopes, vertical cliffs, and overhanging cliffs.

E. Be able to construct topographic profiles and calculate their vertical exaggeration.

F. Understand how stereo pairs (stereograms) of aerial photographs are obtained and used in geological studies.

MATERIALS

Pencil, eraser, laboratory notebook, topographic quadrangle map (obtained by you or provided by your instructor), calculator, and pocket stereoscope (optional); millimeter ruler, protractor, and UTM templates from the GeoTools Sheets.

INTRODUCTION

In 1937, American aviator Amelia Earhart and her navigator Fred Noonan attempted to make the first round-the-world flight. But two-thirds of the way around the globe, they disappeared in the South Pacific Ocean. Earhart and Noonan were trying to reach tiny Howland Island, a mere speck of land just north of the Equator, when they vanished. It appears that their flight plan gave the wrong coordinates for the island.

Earhart's flight plan listed the island's coordinates as 0°49′ north latitude, 176°43′ west longitude. But the actual coordinates are 0°48′ north latitude, 176°38′ west longitude (Barker, V., *New Haven Register*, Dec. 21, 1986:A48). In the open ocean, with nothing else to guide them and limited fuel, such a miss was fatal.

Investigators who researched their disappearance thought that Earhart and Noonan were on course and would certainly have reached Howland Island—had they been given the correct coordinates. Thus, their demise probably was due to a mapmaker's mistake or to the flight planner's inability to correctly read a map.

Earhart's story illustrates that map errors, or errors in map use, can have drastic effects. Your ability to construct, read, and interpret maps is essential for conducting many geologic studies. Geologists generally use aerial photographs in combination with maps to provide additional visual information not given on maps. When used in pairs taken from slightly different angles, aerial photographs allow the geologist to see the ground in stereo.

PART A: INTRODUCTION TO TOPOGRAPHIC MAPS

A **topographic map** is a two-dimensional (flat) representation (model) of a three-dimensional land surface (landscape). It shows landforms (hills, valleys, slopes, coastlines, gullies) and their **relief** (difference in elevation) by using **contour lines** to represent elevations of hills and valleys. The contour lines are the distinguishing features of a topographic map. They are what makes a topographic map different from the more familiar *planimetric* map, such as a highway map, which has no contour lines and does not show relief of the land. The three-dimensional aspect of topographic maps makes them a valuable tool in geological and engineering studies. They also are used by hikers, hunters, campers, developers, planners, and anyone else who needs to know about the topography of a region.

Topographic Quadrangles and Declination

Most United States topographic maps are published by the U.S. Geological Survey (**http://www.usgs.gov**). Most Canadian topographic maps are produced by the Centre for Topographic Information of Natural Resources Canada (**http://maps.nrcan.gc.ca**). Although some topographic maps cover areas defined by political boundaries (such as a state, county, or city), most topographic maps depict rectangular sections of Earth's surface, called quadrangles. A **quadrangle** is a section of Earth's surface that is bounded by lines of *latitude* at the top (north) and bottom (south) and by lines of *longitude* on the left (west) and right (east)—see Figure 1.

Latitude and longitude are both measured in *degrees* (°). Latitude is measured from 0° at the Equator to 90°N (at the North Pole) or 90°S (at the South Pole). Longitude is measured in degrees east or west of the *prime meridian*, a line that runs from the North Pole to the South Pole through Greenwich, England. Locations in Earth's Eastern Hemisphere are east of the prime meridian, and locations in the Western Hemisphere are west of the prime meridian. For finer measurements each degree can be subdivided into 60 equal subdivisions called *minutes* ('), and the minutes can be divided into 60 equal subdivisions called *seconds* (").

Quadrangle maps are published in several sizes, but two are most common: 15-*minute* quadrangle maps and $7\frac{1}{2}$-*minute* quadrangle maps. The numbers refer to the amount of area that the maps depict, in degrees of latitude and longitude. A *15-minute topographic map* represents an area that measures 15 minutes of latitude by 15 minutes of longitude. A $7\frac{1}{2}$-minute topographic map represents an area that measures $7\frac{1}{2}$ minutes of latitude by $7\frac{1}{2}$ minutes of longitude. Each 15-minute map can be divided into four $7\frac{1}{2}$-minute maps (Figure 1).

Because longitude lines form the left and right boundaries of a topographic map, north is always at the top of the quadrangle. This is called grid north (GN) and is usually the same direction as *true north* on the actual Earth. Unfortunately, magnetic compasses are not attracted to true north (the geographic North Pole). Instead, they are attracted to the *magnetic north pole* (MN), currently located northwest of Hudson Bay in Northern Canada, about 700 km (450 mi) from the true North Pole. A compass-like symbol on the bottom margin of topographic maps shows the **declination** (difference in degrees) between compass north (MN) and true north (usually a *star* symbol). Also shown is the declination between compass north (*star* symbol) and grid north (GN). The magnetic pole migrates very slowly, so the declination is exact only for the year listed on the map.

Map Symbols and Revisions

Topographic maps have colors, patterns, and symbols (Figure 2) that are used to depict water bodies, vegetation, roads, buildings, political boundaries, place-names, and other natural and cultural features of the landscape represented by the map (Figure 3).

Additional information is presented in the margins of these maps, including the revision date. Because people constantly change the cultural features on Earth's surface, and because Earth's surface itself occasionally changes rapidly from events such as

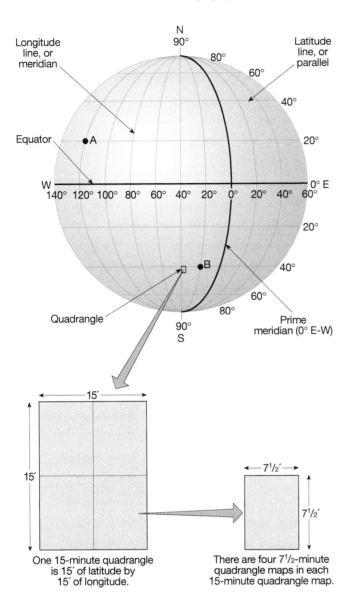

One 15-minute quadrangle is 15′ of latitude by 15′ of longitude.

There are four 7½-minute quadrangle maps in each 15-minute quadrangle map.

FIGURE 1 Latitude and longitude geographic grid and coordinate system. Earth's spherical surface is divided into lines of latitude (*parallels*) that go around the world parallel to the Equator, and lines of longitude (*meridians*) that go around the world from pole to pole. There are 360 degrees (360°) around the entire Earth, so the distance from the Equator to a pole (one-fourth of the way around Earth) is 90° of latitude. The Equator is assigned a value of zero degrees (0°) latitude, the North Pole is 90 degrees North latitude (90° N), and the South Pole is 90 degrees south latitude (90° S). The *prime meridian* is zero degrees of longitude and runs from pole to pole through Greenwich, England. Locations in Earth's Eastern Hemisphere are located in degrees east of the prime meridian, and points in the Western Hemisphere are in located in degrees west of the prime meridian. Therefore, any point on Earth (or a map) can be located by its latitude-longitude coordinates. The latitude coordinate of the point is its position in degrees north or south of the Equator. The longitude coordinate of the point is its position in degrees east or west of the Prime Meridian. For example, point **A** is located at coordinates of: 20° North latitude, 120° West longitude.

For greater detail, each degree of latitude and longitude can also be subdivided into 60 minutes (60′), and each minute can be divided into 60 seconds (60″). Note that a 15-minute (15′) quadrangle map represents an area of Earth's surface that is 15 minutes of longitude wide (E-W) and 15 minutes of latitude long (N-S). A 7.5-minute quadrangle map is one-fourth of a 15-minute quadrangle map.

landslides and floods, the maps must be updated. This is done by *photorevision*. Aerial photographs are used to discover changes on the landscape, and the changes are overprinted on the maps in a standout color like purple, red, or gray.

Contour Lines

Examine the image of one of the Galapagos Islands in Figure 4, a perspective view of the landscape that has been false colored to show relief. It was made by transmitting imaging radar from an airplane (flying at a constant altitude). Timed pulses of the radar measured the distance between the airplane (flying at a constant elevation) and the ground. Overlapping

pulses of the radar produced the three-dimensional perspective similar to the way that overlapping lines of sight from your eyes enable you to see in stereo. Notice that the island has a distinct coastline, which has the same elevation all of the way around the island (zero feet above sea level). Similarly, all points at the very top of the green (including yellow-green) regions form a line at about 300 ft above sea level. These lines of equal elevation (i.e., the coastline and 300-ft line) are called **contour lines.** Unfortunately, the 1200-ft contour line (located at the boundary between yellow and pink) is not visible behind Darwin and Wolf Volcanoes in this perspective view. The only way that you could see all of the 0-ft, 300-ft, and 1200-ft contour lines at the same time would be if you viewed

FIGURE 2 Symbols used on topographic quadrangle maps produced by the U.S. Geological Survey.

Primary highway, hard surface	
Secondary highway, hard surface	
Light-duty road, hard or improved surface	
Unimproved road	
Road under construction, alinement known	
Proposed road	
Dual highway, dividing strip 25 feet or less	
Dual highway, dividing strip exceeding 25 feet	
Trail	

Railroad: single track and multiple track	
Railroads in juxtaposition	
Narrow gage: single track and multiple track	
Railroad in street and carline	
Bridge: road and railroad	
Drawbridge: road and railroad	
Footbridge	
Tunnel: road and railroad	
Overpass and underpass	
Small masonry or concrete dam	
Dam with lock	
Dam with road	
Canal with lock	

Buildings (dwelling, place of employment, etc.)	
School, church, and cemetery	Cem
Buildings (barn, warehouse, etc.)	
Power transmission line with located metal tower	
Telephone line, pipeline, etc. (labeled as to type)	
Wells other than water (labeled as to type)	oOil .... oGas
Tanks: oil, water, etc. (labeled only if water)	• • ● ⊘Water
Located or landmark object; windmill	o
Open pit, mine, or quarry; prospect	✕ X
Shaft and tunnel entrance	◾ .... Y

Horizontal and vertical control station:

Tablet, spirit level elevation	BM △ 5653
Other recoverable mark, spirit level elevation	△ 5455
Horizontal control station: tablet, vertical angle elevation	VABM △ 9519
Any recoverable mark, vertical angle or checked elevation	△3775
Vertical control station: tablet, spirit level elevation	BM ✕957
Other recoverable mark, spirit level elevation	✕954
Spot elevation	✕ 7369
Water elevation	670 670

Boundaries: National	
State	
County, parish, municipio	
Civil township, precinct, town, barrio	
Incorporated city, village, town, hamlet	
Reservation, National or State	
Small park, cemetery, airport, etc.	
Land grant	
Township or range line, United States land survey	
Township or range line, approximate location	
Section line, United States land survey	
Section line, approximate location	
Township line, not United States land survey	
Section line, not United States land survey	
Found corner: section and closing	
Boundary monument: land grant and other	□ .... □
Fence or field line	

Index contour	Intermediate contour
Supplementary contour	Depression contours
Fill	Cut
Levee	Levee with road
Mine dump	Wash
Tailings	Tailings pond
Shifting sand or dunes	Intricate surface
Sand area	Gravel beach

Perennial streams	Intermittent streams
Elevated aqueduct	Aqueduct tunnel
Water well and spring	Glacier
Small rapids	Small falls
Large rapids	Large falls
Intermittent lake	Dry lake bed
Foreshore flat	Rock or coral reef
Sounding, depth curve	Piling or dolphin
Exposed wreck	Sunken wreck
Rock, bare or awash; dangerous to navigation	

Marsh (swamp)	Submerged marsh
Wooded marsh	Mangrove
Woods or brushwood	Orchard
Vineyard	Scrub
Land subject to controlled inundation	Urban area

58

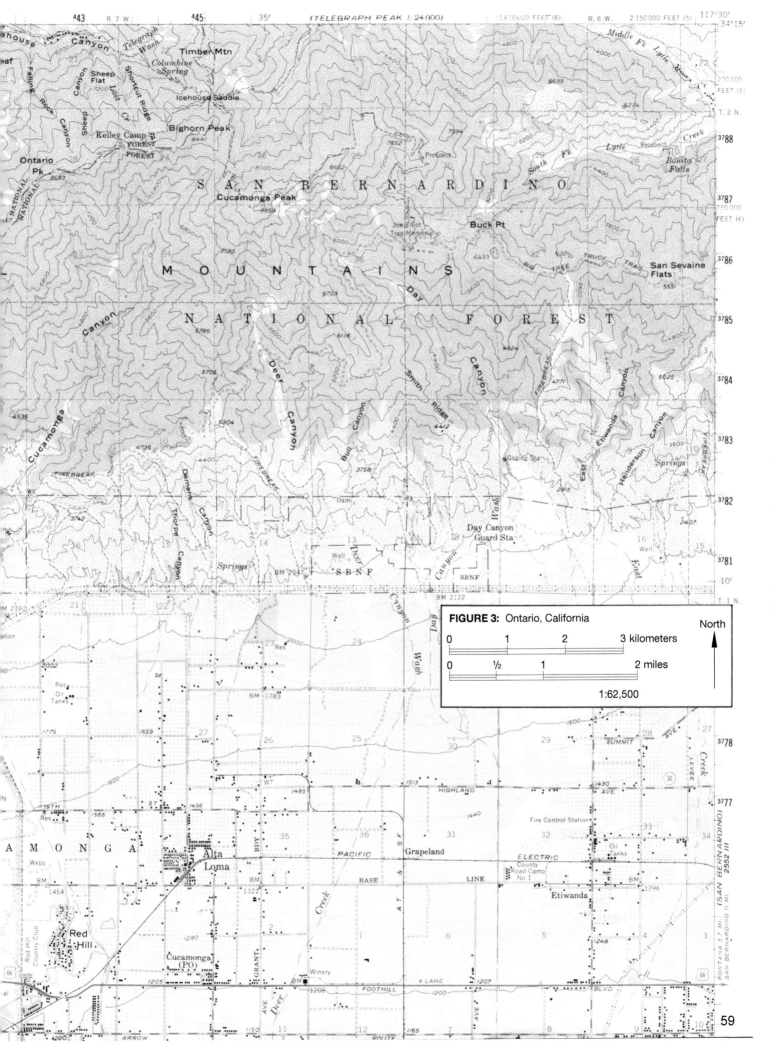

FIGURE 3: Ontario, California

North

| 0 | | 1 | | 2 | | 3 kilometers |

| 0 | ½ | | 1 | | 2 miles |

1:62,500

59

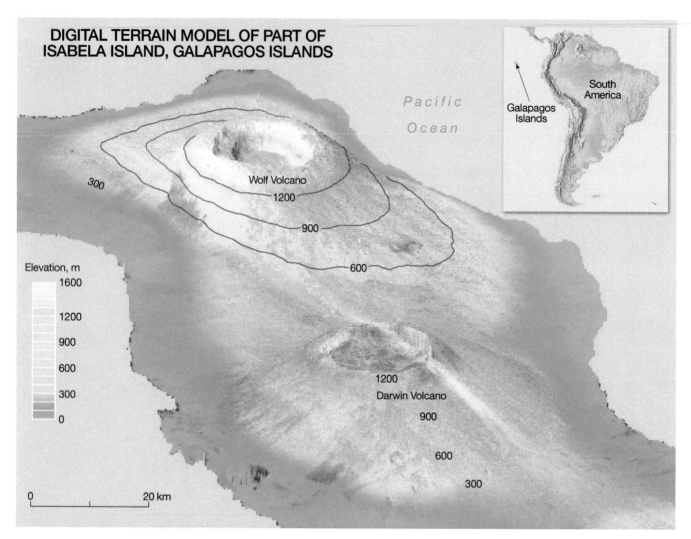

FIGURE 4   Digital model (AIRSAR/TOPSAR 3-dimensional perspective) of part of Isabela Island, Galapagos Islands. The image has been false-colored to show relief. It was made with imaging radar transmitted from an airplane (flying at a constant altitude of 33,000 ft). Timed pulses of the radar measured the distance between the airplane (flying at a constant elevation) and the ground. Overlapping pulses of the radar produced the three-dimensional perspective. See if you can draw the remaining 300-, 600-, 900-, and 1200-foot contour lines. (Image courtesy of NASA/JPL–Caltech)

the island from directly above. This is how topographic maps are constructed (Figure 5).

Topographic maps are made from overlapping pairs of photographs, called *stereo pairs*. Each stereo pair is taken from an airplane making two closely-spaced passes over a region at the same elevation. The passes are flown far enough apart to provide the stereo effect, yet close enough to be almost directly above the land that is to be mapped. After the stereo pairs are used to define contour lines and construct a first draft of the topographic map, angular distortion is removed and the exact elevations of the contour lines on the map are "ground truthed" (checked on the ground) using very precise altimeters and GPS.

Therefore, topographic maps are miniature models of Earth's three-dimensional surface, printed on two-dimensional pieces of paper. Two of the dimensions are the lengths and widths of objects and landscape features. But the third dimension, elevation (height), is shown using contour lines. Each **contour line** connects all points on the map that have the same elevation above sea level (Figure 6, rule 1). Look at the topographic map in Figure 3 and notice the light brown and heavy brown contour lines. The heavy brown contour lines are called **index contours,** because they have elevations printed on them (whereas the lighter contour lines do not; Figure 6, rule 6). Index contours are your starting point when reading

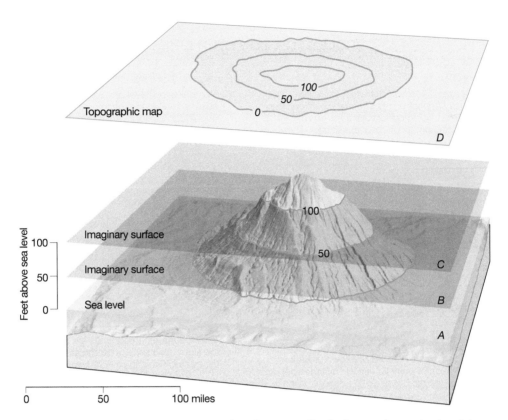

FIGURE 5 Topographic map construction. A *contour line* is drawn where a horizontal plane (such as **A**, **B**, or **C**) intersects the land surface. Where sea level (plane **A**) intersects the land, it forms the 0-ft contour line. Plane **B** is 50 ft above sea level, so its intersection with the land is the 50-ft contour line. Plane **C** is 100 ft above sea level, so its intersection with the land is the 100-foot contour line. **D** is the resulting topographic map of the island. It was constructed by looking down onto the island from above and tracing the 0, 50, and 100-ft contour lines. The elevation change between any two contour lines is 50 ft, so the map is said to have a 50-ft *contour interval*. The topographic datum (reference level) is sea level, so all contour lines on this map represent elevations in feet above sea level and are *topographic contour lines*. (Contours below sea level are called *bathymetric contour lines* and are generally shown in blue).

elevations on a topographic map. For example, notice that every fifth contour line on Figure 3 is an index contour. Also notice that the index contours are labeled with elevations in increments of 400 ft. This means that the map has five contours for every 400 ft of elevation, or a **contour interval** of 80 ft. The contour interval is specified on most topographic maps in feet or meters. All contour lines are multiples of the contour interval above a specific surface (almost always sea level). For example, if a map uses a 10-ft contour interval, then the contour lines represent elevations of 0 ft (sea level), 10 ft, 20 ft, 30 ft, 40 ft, and so on. Most maps use the smallest contour interval that will allow easy readability and provide as much detail as possible.

Additional rules for contour lines are provided in Figure 6. For example, contour lines never cross, except in the rare case where an overhanging cliff is present. If contour lines merge into one line, then that line indicates a cliff. The spacing of contour lines can be used to interpret the steepness of a slope and whether it is uniform or variable in steepness. The apex (tip) of a V-shaped notch in a contour line always points up hill.

Be sure to review all of the rules for contour lines in Figure 6 and the common kinds of landforms represented by contour lines on topographic maps (Figure 7). Your ability to use a topographic map is based on your ability to interpret what the contour lines mean.

RULES FOR CONTOUR LINES

1. Every point on a contour line is of the exact same elevation; that is, contour lines connect points of equal elevation. The contour lines are constructed by surveying the elevation of points, then connecting points of equal elevation.

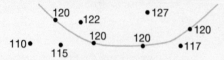

2. Interpolation is used to estimate the elevation of a point B located in line between points A and C of known elevation. To estimate the elevation of point B:

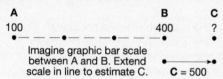

3. Extrapolation is used to estimate the elevations of a point C located in line beyond points A and B of known elevation. To estimate the elevation of point C, use the distance between A and B as a ruler or graphic bar scale to estimate in line to elevation C.

A				**B**	**C**
100				400	?

Imagine graphic bar scale between A and B. Extend scale in line to estimate C. **C = 500**

4. Contour lines always separate points of higher elevation (uphill) from points of lower elevation (downhill). You must determine which direction on the map is higher and which is lower, relative to the contour line in question, by checking adjacent elevations.

5. Contour lines always close to form an irregular circle. But sometimes part of a contour line extends beyond the mapped area so that you cannot see the entire circle formed.

6. The elevation between any two adjacent contour lines of different elevation on a topographic map is the *contour interval*. Often every fifth contour line is heavier so that you can count by five times the contour interval. These heavier contour lines are known as *index contours*, because they generally have elevations printed on them.

7. Contour lines never cross each other except for one rare case: where an overhanging cliff is present. In such a case, the hidden contours are dashed.

8. Contour lines can merge to form a single contour line only where there is a vertical cliff or wall.

Vertical cliff

9. Evenly spaced contour lines of different elevation represent a uniform slope.

10. The closer the contour lines are to each other the steeper the slope. In other words, the steeper the slope the closer the contour lines.

Steep — Less steep

11. A concentric series of closed contours represents a hill:

12. *Depression contours* have hachure marks on the downhill side and represent a closed depression:

See Figure 8

13. Contour lines form a V pattern when crossing streams. The apex of the V always points upstream (uphill):

Uphill

Apex (tip) of the V

downstream (downhill)

14. Contour lines that occur on opposite sides of a valley or ridge always occur in pairs. See Figure 9.

FIGURE 6   Rules for constructing and interpreting contour lines on topographic maps.

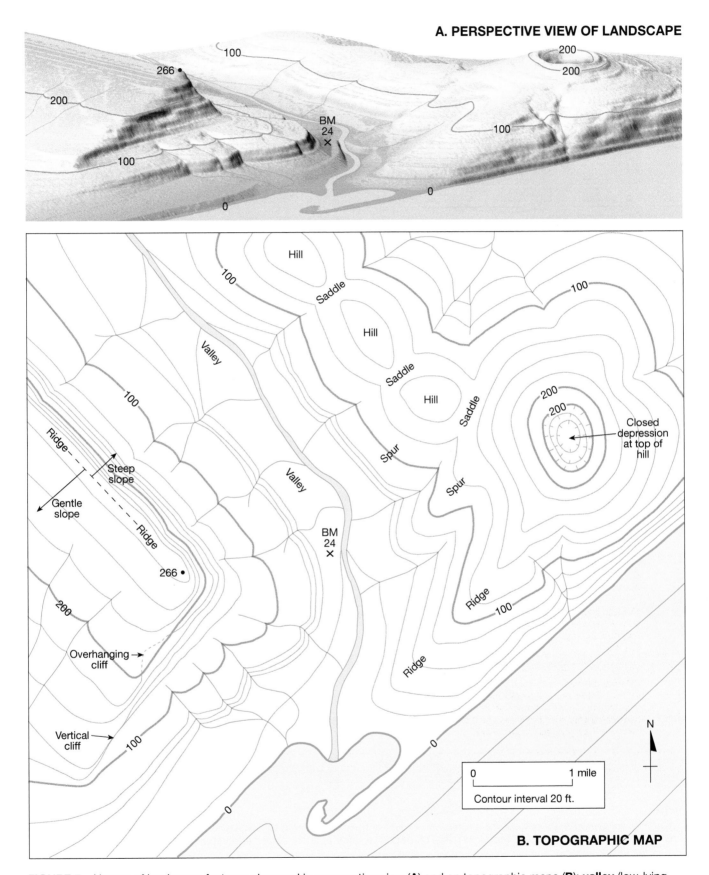

A. PERSPECTIVE VIEW OF LANDSCAPE

B. TOPOGRAPHIC MAP

FIGURE 7 Names of landscape features observed in perspective view (**A**) and on topographic maps (**B**): **valley** (low-lying land bordered by higher ground), **hill** (rounded elevation of land; mound), **ridge** (linear or elongate elevation or crest of land), **spur** (short ridge or branch of a main ridge), **saddle** (low point in a ridge or line of hills; it resembles a horse saddle), **closed depression** (low point/area in a landscape from which surface water cannot drain; contour lines with hachure marks), **steep slope** (closely-spaced contour lines), **gentle slope** (widely-spaced contour lines), **vertical cliff** (merged contour lines), **overhanging cliff** (dashed contour line that crosses a solid one; the dashed line indicates what is under the overhanging cliff).

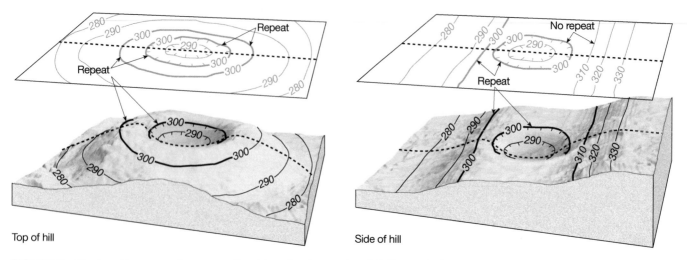

Top of hill

Side of hill

FIGURE 8 Contour lines repeat on opposite sides of a depression (left illustration), except when the depression occurs on a slope (right illustration).

Reading Elevations

If a point lies on an index contour, you simply read its elevation from that line. If the point lies on an un-numbered contour line, then its elevation can be determined by counting up or down from the nearest index contour. For example, if the nearest index contour is 300 ft, and your point of interest is on the fourth contour line *above* it, and the contour interval is 20 ft, then you simply count up by 20s from the index

contour: 320, 340, 360, 380. The point is 380 ft above sea level. (Or, if the point is three contour lines *below* the index contour, you count down: 280, 260, 240; the point is 240 ft above sea level.)

If a point lies between two contour lines, then you must estimate its elevation by interpolation (Figure 6, rule 2). For example, on a map with a 20-ft contour interval, a point might lie between the 340 and 360-ft contours, so you know it is between 340 and 360 ft above sea level. If a point lies between a contour line

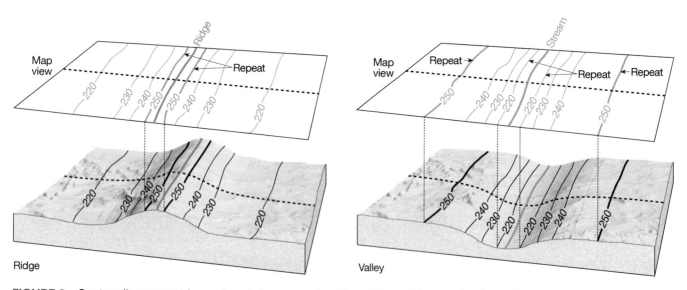

Ridge

Valley

FIGURE 9 Contour lines repeat (occur in pairs) on opposite sides of linear ridges and valleys. For example, in the left illustration, if you walked the dashed line from left to right, you would cross the 220, 230, 240 and 250-ft contour lines, go over the crest of the ridge, and cross the 250, 240, 230, and 220-ft contour lines again as you walk down the other side. Note that the 250-ft contour lines on these maps are heavier than the other lines because they are *index contours*. On most maps every fifth contour line above sea level is an index contour, so you can count by five times the contour interval. The *contour interval* (elevation between any two contour lines) of these maps is 10 ft, so the index contours are every 50 feet of elevation.

and the margin of the map, then you must estimate its elevation by extrapolation (Figure 6, rule 3).

Figure 8 shows how to read topographic contour lines in and adjacent to a depression. *Hachure marks* (short line segments pointing downhill) on some of the contour lines in these maps indicate the presence of a closed depression (a depression from which water cannot drain) (Figure 6, rule 12). At the top of a hill, contour lines repeat on opposite sides of the rim of the depression. On the side of a hill, the contour lines repeat only on the downhill side of the depression.

Figure 9 shows how topographic contour lines represent linear ridge crests and valley bottoms. Ridges and valleys are roughly symmetrical, so individual contour lines repeat on each side (Figure 6, rule 14). To visualize this, picture yourself walking along an imaginary trail across the ridge or valley (dashed lines in Figure 9). Every time you walk up the side of a hill or valley, you cross contour lines. Then, when you walk down the other side of the hill or valley, you recross contour lines of the same elevations as those crossed walking uphill.

Elevations of specific points on topographic maps (tops of peaks, bridges, survey points, etc.) sometimes are indicated directly on the maps beside the symbols indicated for that purpose. The notation "BM" denotes a **benchmark,** a permanent marker (usually a metal plate) placed by the U.S. Geological Survey or Bureau of Land Management at the point indicated on the map (Figure 2). Elevations usually are given. For example, look at the middle map in Figure 10. At the top center part of the map is an "x" symbol labeled "BM 463," indicating that "x" marks the location of the benchmark that was exactly 463 ft above sea level at the time of its placement. Two other benchmarks also appear on this map: BM 360 and BM 261.

The elevations of prominent hilltops, peaks, or other features are sometimes identified specifically, even if there is no benchmark on the ground. For example, the highest point on the ridge in the west central part of Figure 7B has an elevation of 266 ft above sea level.

Relief and Gradient

Recall that **relief** is the difference in elevation between landforms, specific points, or other features on a landscape or map. *Regional relief* is the difference in elevation between the highest and lowest points on a topographic map. The highest point is the top of the highest hill or mountain; the lowest point is generally where the major stream of the area leaves the map, or a coastline. **Gradient** is a measure of the steepness of

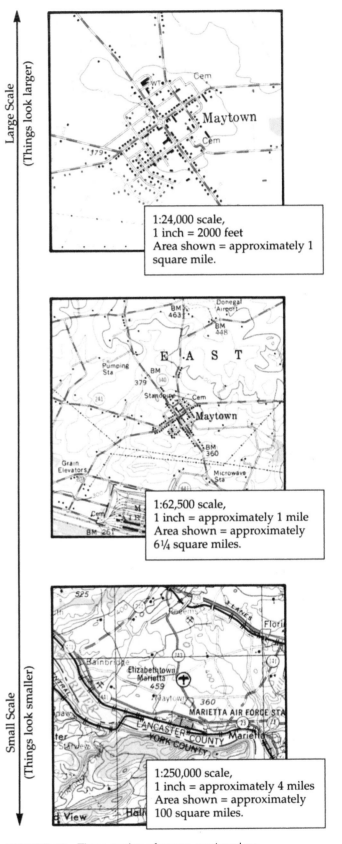

FIGURE 10 Three scales of maps, centered on Maytown. Notice that everything looks small on the small-scale map. Everything looks larger on the large-scale map.

a slope. One way to determine and express the gradient of a slope is by measuring its steepness as an angle of ascent or descent (expressed in degrees). On a topographic map, gradient is usually determined by dividing the relief (rise or fall) between two points on the map by the distance (run) between them (expressed as a fraction in feet per mile or meters per kilometer). For example, if points **A** and **B** on a map have elevations of 200 ft and 300 ft, and the points are located two miles apart, then:

$$\text{gradient} = \frac{\text{relief (amount of rise or fall between } \mathbf{A} \text{ and } \mathbf{B})}{\text{distance between } \mathbf{A} \text{ and } \mathbf{B}}$$

$$= \frac{100 \text{ ft}}{2 \text{ mi}} = 50 \text{ ft/mi}$$

Scales of Maps and Models

Maps are scale models, like toy cars or boats. To make a model of anything, you must first establish a model scale. This is the proportion by which you will reduce the real object to the model size. For example, if you make a $\frac{1}{4}$-scale model of a 16-ft car, your model would be 4 ft long. The ratio scale of model-to-object is 4:16, which reduces to 1:4. A house floorplan, which really is a map of a house, commonly is drawn so that one foot on the plan equals 30 or 40 ft of real house, or a **ratio scale** of 1:30 or 1:40.

Topographic maps often model large portions of Earth's surface, so the ratio scale must be much greater—like 1:24,000. This ratio scale can also be expressed as a **fractional scale** (1/24,000), indicating that the portion of Earth represented has been reduced to the fraction of 1/24,000th of its actual size.

Therefore, a *ratio scale* of 1:24,000 equals a *fractional scale* of 1/24,000. They both are ways of indicating that any unit (inch, centimeter, foot, etc.) on the map represents 24,000 of the same units (inches, centimeters, feet) on Earth's surface. For example, 1 cm on the map represents 24,000 cm on the ground, or your thumb width on the map represents 24,000 thumb widths on the ground. Other common map scales are 1:25,000, 1:50,000, 1:62,500, 1:63,360, 1:100,000, 1:125,000, and 1:250,000. Figure 10 shows how maps at different scales show the same region but present different amounts of detail and area.

Drawing a map at 1:24,000 scale provides a very useful amount of detail. But knowing that 1 inch on the map = 24,000 inches on the ground is not very convenient, because no one measures big distances in inches! However, if you divide the 24,000 inches by 12 to get 2000 ft, the scale suddenly becomes useful: "1 in. on the map = 2000 ft on the ground." An

American football field is 100 yards (300 ft) long, so: "1 in. on the map = $6\frac{2}{3}$ football fields." Such scales expressed with words are called **verbal scales.**

On a map with a scale of 1:63,360, 1 in. = 63,360 in., again not meaningful in daily use. But there are 63,360 in. in a mile. So, the verbal scale, "1 in. = 1 mi," is very meaningful. A standard 1:62,500 map (15-minute quadrangle map) is very close to this scale, so it is common practice to say that "one inch equals approximately one mile" on such a map. Note that verbal scales are often approximate because their sole purpose is to increase the convenience of using a map.

Finally, all topographic maps have one or more **graphic bar scales** printed in their lower margin. They are essentially rulers for measuring distances on the map. U.S. Geological Survey topographic maps generally have four different bar scales: miles, feet, kilometers, and meters.

PLS—Public Land Survey System

The **U.S. Public Land Survey System (PLS)** was initiated in the late 1700s. All but the original thirteen states, and a few states derived from them, are covered by this system. Other exceptions occur in the southwestern United States, where land surveys may be based upon Spanish land grants, and in areas of rugged terrain that were never surveyed.

The PLS scheme was established in each state by surveying **principal meridians,** which are north–south lines, and **base lines,** which are east–west lines (Figure 11A). Once the initial principal meridian and base lines were established, additional lines were surveyed parallel to them and six miles apart. This created a grid of 6 mi by 6 mi squares of land. The north–south squares of the grid are called **townships** and are numbered relative to the base line (Township 1 North, Township 2 North, etc.). The east–west squares of the grid are **ranges** and are numbered relative to the principal meridian (Range 1 West, Range 2 West, etc.). Each 6 mi by 6 mi square is, therefore, identified by its township and range position in the PLS grid. For example, the square in Figure 11B is located at T1S (Township 1 South) and R2W (Range 2 West). Although each square like this is identified as both a township and a range within the PLS grid, it is common practice to refer to the squares as townships rather than township-and-ranges.

Townships are used as political subdivisions in some states and are often given placenames. Each township square is also divided into 36 small squares,

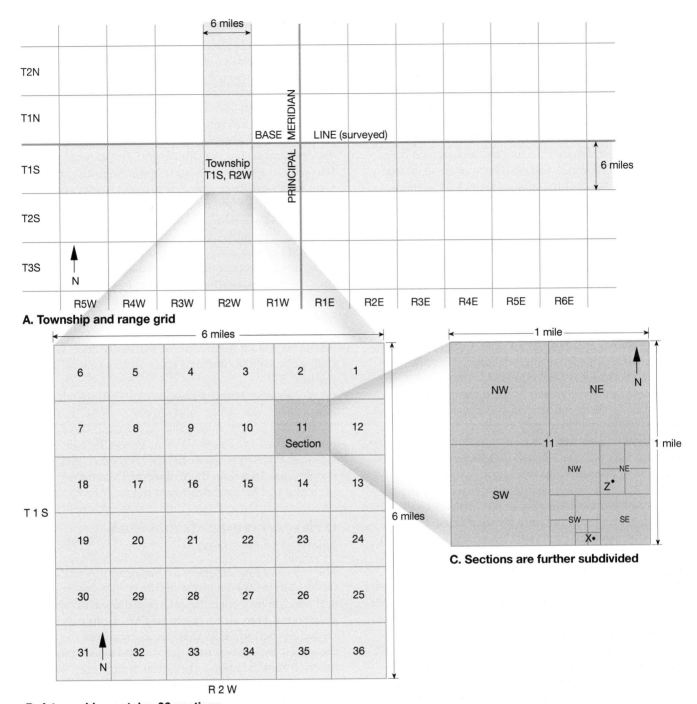

A. Township and range grid

B. A township contains 36 sections

C. Sections are further subdivided

FIGURE 11 U.S. Public Land Survey System (PLS) is based on a grid of townships and ranges unique to specific states or regions. **A.** Townships and ranges are located relative to a state's *principal meridian* (N-S line) of longitude and its *base line* (E-W line, surveyed perpendicular to the principal meridian). *Township* strips (columns) of land are 6 miles long and parallel to the base line. North of the base line, townships are numbered T1N, T2N, and so on. South of the base line, townships are numbered T1S, T2S, and so on. *Range* strips (rows) of land are 6 miles wide and parallel to the principal meridian. East of the principal meridian, ranges are numbered R1E, R2E, and so on. West of the principal meridian, ranges are numbered R1W, R2W, and so on. Each intersection of a township strip of land with a range strip of land forms a square, called a *township.* Note the location of Township T1S, R2W. **B.** Each township is 6 miles wide and 6 miles long, so it contains 36 square miles. Each square mile (640 acres) is called a *section,* and each section is numbered exactly as shown above. **C.** Sections are subdivided according to a hierarchy of square *quarters* listed in order of increasing size and direction. For example, point **x** is located in the southeast quarter, of the southeast quarter, of the southwest quarter, of the southeast quarter, of section 11. This is written: SE_4^1, SE_4^1, SW_4^1, SE_4^1, sec. 11, T1S, R2W.

each having an area of 1 square mile (640 acres). These squares are called **sections.**

Sections are numbered from 1 to 36, beginning in the upper right corner (Figure 11B). Sometimes these are shown on topographic quadrangle maps (Figure 3, red grid). Any point can be located precisely within a section by dividing the section into quarters (labeled NW, NE, SW, SE). Each of these quarters can itself be subdivided into quarters and labeled (Figure 11C).

GPS—Global Positioning System

The **Global Positioning System (GPS)** is a constellation of 28 navigational communication satellites in 12-hour orbits approximately 12,000 miles above Earth (about 24 of these are operational at any given time). The GPS constellation is maintained by the United States (NOAA and NASA) for operations of the U.S. Department of Defense, but it is free for anyone to use. Since GPS receivers can be purchased for as little as $100, they are widely used by airplane navigators, automated vehicle navigation systems, ship captains, hikers, and scientists to map locations on Earth. More expensive and accurate receivers with millimeter accuracy are used for space-based geodesy measurements that reveal plate motions over time.

Each GPS satellite communicates simultaneously with fixed ground-based Earth stations and other GPS satellites, so it knows exactly where it is located relative to the center of Earth and Universal Time Coordinated (UTC, also called Greenwich Mean Time). Each GPS satellite also transmits its own radio signal on a different channel, which can be detected by a fixed or handheld GPS receiver. If you turn on a handheld GPS receiver in an unobstructed outdoor location, then the receiver immediately *acquires* (picks up) the radio channel of the strongest signal it can detect from a GPS satellite. It downloads the navigational information from that satellite channel, followed by a second, third, and so on. A receiver must acquire and process radio transmissions from at least four GPS satellites to triangulate a determination of its exact position and elevation—this is known as a *fix.*

Most newer models of GPS receivers are *12 channel parallel receivers,* which means they can receive and process radio signals from as many as twelve satellites at the same time (the maximum possible number for any point on Earth). Older models cycle through the channels one at a time, or have fewer parallel channels, so they take longer to process data and usually give less accurate results. An unobstructed view is also best (GPS receivers cannot operate indoors). If the path from satellite to receiver is obstructed by

trees, canyon walls, or buildings, then the receiver has difficulty acquiring that radio signal. It is also possible that more or fewer satellites will be nearly overhead at one time than another, because they are in constant motion within the constellation. Therefore, if you cannot obtain a fix at one time (because four satellite channels cannot be acquired), you may be able to obtain a fix in another half hour or so. Acquiring more than four satellite channels will provide more navigational data and more accurate results. Most handheld, 12-channel parallel receivers have an accuracy of about 10–15 meters.

When using a GPS receiver for the first time in a new region, it generally takes about one to three minutes for it to triangulate a fix. This information is stored in the receiver, so readings taken over the next few hours at nearby locations normally take only seconds. Consult the operational manual for your receiver so you know the time it normally takes for a *cold* fix (first time) or *warm* fix (within a few hours of the last fix).

GPS navigation does not rely on the latitude-longitude or the public land survey system. It relies on an Earth-centered geographic grid and coordinate system called the *World Geodetic System 1984* or *WGS 84. WGS 84* is a **datum** (survey or navigational framework) based on the Universal Transverse Mercator (UTM) grid described below.

UTM—Universal Transverse Mercator System

The U.S. National Imagery and Mapping Agency (NIMA) developed a global military navigation grid and coordinate system in 1947 called the **Universal Transverse Mercator System (UTM).** Unlike the latitude-longitude grid that is spherical and measured in degrees, minutes, seconds, and nautical miles (1 nautical mile = 1 minute of latitude), the UTM grid is rectangular and measured in decimal-based metric units (meters).

The UTM grid (top of Figure 12) is based on sixty north–south **zones,** which are strips of longitude having a width of 6°. The zones are consecutively numbered from Zone 01 (between 180° and 174° west longitude) at the left margin of the grid, to Zone 60 (between 174° and 180° east longitude) at the east margin of the grid. The location of a point within a zone is defined by its **easting** coordinate—its distance within the zone measured in meters from west to east, and a **northing** coordinate—its distance from the Equator measured in meters. In the Northern Hemisphere, northings are given in meters north of the Equator. To avoid negative numbers for northings in

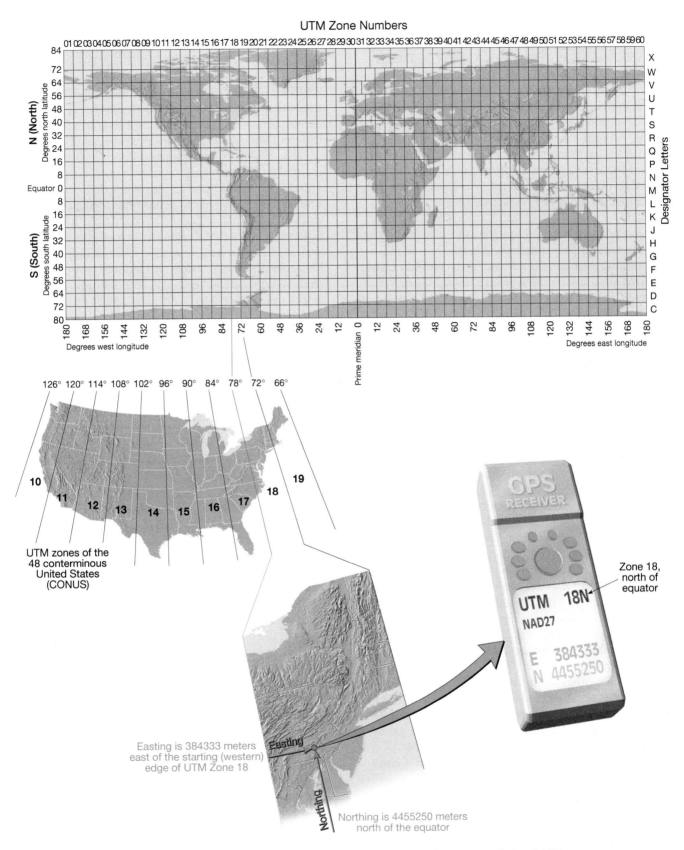

UTM Zone Numbers

FIGURE 12 UTM and GPS. A handheld Global Positioning System (GPS) receiver operated at point **X** indicates its location according to the Universal Transverse Mercator (UTM) grid and coordinate system, *North American Datum 1927* (*NAD27*). Refer to text for explanation.

the Southern Hemisphere, NIMA assigned the Equator a reference northing of 10,000,000 meters.

Since satellites did not exist until 1957, and GPS navigational satellites did not exist until decades later, the UTM grid was applied for many years using regional ground-based surveys to determine locations of the grid boundaries. Each of these regional or continental surveys is called a **datum** and is identified on the basis of its location and the year it was surveyed. Examples include *North American Datum 1927 (NAD27)* and *North American Datum 1983 (NAD83)*, which appear on many Canadian and U.S. Geological Survey topographic quadrangle maps. The Global Positioning System relies on an Earth-centered UTM datum called the *World Geodetic System 1984* or *WGS 84*, but GPS receivers can be set up to display regional datums like *NAD27*. When using GPS with a topographic map, be sure to set the GPS receiver to display the UTM datum of that map.

Study the illustration of a GPS receiver in Figure 12. Notice that the receiver is displaying UTM coordinates (based on *NAD27*) for a point **X** in Zone 18 (north of the Equator). Point **X** has an easting coordinate of E384333, which means that it is located 384333 meters east of the starting (west) edge of Zone 18. Point **X** also has a northing coordinate of N4455250, which means that it is located 4455250 meters north of the Equator. Therefore, Point **X** is located in southeast Pennsylvania. To plot Point **X** on a 1:24,000 scale, $7\frac{1}{2}$ minute topographic quadrangle map, see Figure 13.

Point **X** is located within the Lititz, PA $7\frac{1}{2}$ Minute Series (USGS, 1:24,000 scale) topographic quadrangle map (Figure 13). Information printed on the map margin indicates that the map has blue ticks spaced 1000 m apart along its edges that conform to *NAD27*, Zone 18. Notice how the ticks for northings (blue) and eastings (green) are represented on the northwest corner of the Lititz map—Figure 13B. One northing label is written out in full ($^{44}56^{000m}$ N) and one easting label is written out in full ($^{3}84^{000m}$ E), but the other values are given in UTM shorthand for thousands of meters (i.e., do not end in^{000m}). Since Point **X** has an easting of E384333 within Zone 18, it must be located 333 m east of the tick mark labeled $^{3}84^{000m}$ E along the top margin of the map. Since Point **X** has a northing of N4455250, it must be located 250 m north of the tick mark labeled as $^{44}55$ in UTM shorthand. Distances east and north can be measured using a ruler and the map's graphic bar scale as a reference (333 m = 0.333 km, 250 m = 0.250 km). However, you can also use the graphic bar scale to construct a UTM grid like the one in Figure 13C. If you construct such a grid and print it onto a transparency, then you can use it as a UTM *grid overlay*. To plot a point or determine its coordinates, place the grid overlay on top of the square kilometer in which the point is located. Then use the grid as a two- dimensional ruler for the northing and easting. If GeoTools Sheets accompany your lab manual, grid overlays for many different scales of UTM grids are provided here.

The UTM system described above is known as the *civilian UTM grid and coordinate system,* and it is the system you should use in your work in this manual. The U.S. Department of Defense has modified this civilian UTM grid to form a Military Grid Reference System (MGRS) that divides the zones into horizontal sections identified by *designator letters* (Figure 12). These sections are 8° wide and lettered consecutively from **C** (between 80° and 72° south latitude) through **X** (between 72° and 84° north latitude). Letters I and O are not used.

Compass Bearings

A **bearing** is the *compass direction* along a line from one point to another. If expressed in degrees east or west of true north or south, it is called a *quadrant bearing*. Or it may be expressed in degrees between 0 and 360, called an *azimuth bearing*, where north is 0° (or 360°), east is 90°, south is 180°, and west is 270°. Linear geologic features (faults, fractures, dikes), lines of sight and travel, and linear property boundaries are all defined on the basis of their bearings.

Remember that a compass points to Earth's *magnetic north* (MN) pole rather than the *grid north* (GN) pole that was used to construct the UTM and latitude-longitude grids of a map. Therefore, a diagram at the margin of every topographic map shows the *declination* (degrees of difference) between MN and GN. If the MN arrow is to the right of GN, then subtract the degrees of declination from your compass reading. If the MN arrow is to the left of GN, then add the degrees of declination to your compass reading. These adjustments will mean that your compass readings are synchronized with the map. However, the magnetic pole migrates very slowly, so the declination is exact only for the year listed on the map.

To determine a compass bearing on a map, draw a straight line from the starting point to the destination point and also through any one of the map's borders. Align a protractor (left drawing, Figure 14) or the N–S or E–W directional axis of a compass (right drawing, Figure 14) with the map's border, and read the bearing in degrees toward the direction of the destination. Imagine that you are buying a property for your dream home. The boundary of the property is marked by four metal rods driven into the ground,

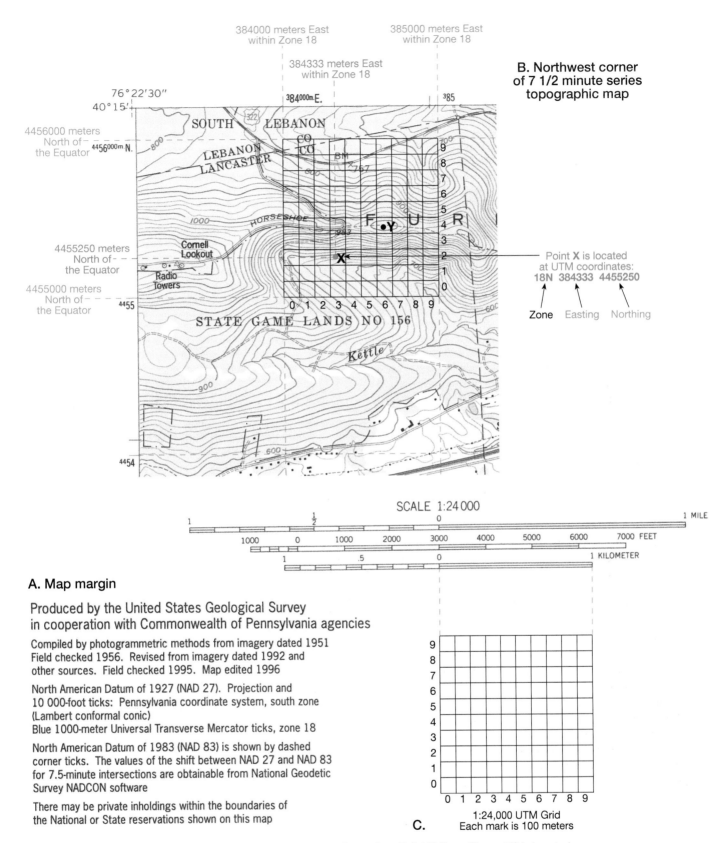

B. Northwest corner
of 7 1/2 minute series
topographic map

SCALE 1:24 000

A. Map margin

Produced by the United States Geological Survey
in cooperation with Commonwealth of Pennsylvania agencies

Compiled by photogrammetric methods from imagery dated 1951
Field checked 1956. Revised from imagery dated 1992 and
other sources. Field checked 1995. Map edited 1996

North American Datum of 1927 (NAD 27). Projection and
10 000-foot ticks: Pennsylvania coordinate system, south zone
(Lambert conformal conic)
Blue 1000-meter Universal Transverse Mercator ticks, zone 18

North American Datum of 1983 (NAD 83) is shown by dashed
corner ticks. The values of the shift between NAD 27 and NAD 83
for 7.5-minute intersections are obtainable from National Geodetic
Survey NADCON software

There may be private inholdings within the boundaries of
the National or State reservations shown on this map

1:24,000 UTM Grid
C. Each mark is 100 meters

FIGURE 13 UTM and topographic maps—refer to text for discussion. Point **X** (from Figure 12) is located within the Lititz, PA 7$\frac{1}{2}$ Minute Series (USGS, 1:24,000 scale) topographic quadrangle map. **A.** Map margin indicates that the map includes UTM grid data based on *North American Datum 1927* (*NAD27*, Zone 18) and represented by blue ticks spaced 1000 meters (1 km) apart along the map edges. **B.** Connect the blue 1000 m ticks to form a grid square, each representing 1 square kilometer. Northings (blue) are read along the N-S map edge, and eastings (green) are located along the E-W map edge. **C.** You can construct a 1 km grid (1:24,000 scale) from the map's bar scale, then make a transparency of it to form a grid overlay. Place the grid overlay atop the 1-kilometer square on the map that includes point **X**, and determine the *NAD27* coordinates of **X** as shown (red).

READING BEARINGS WITH A PROTRACTOR

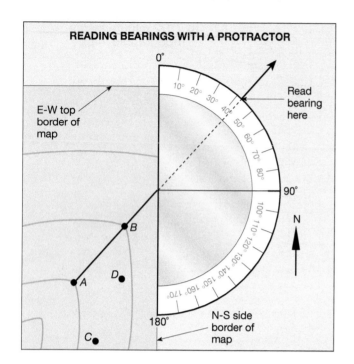

READING BEARINGS WITH A COMPASS

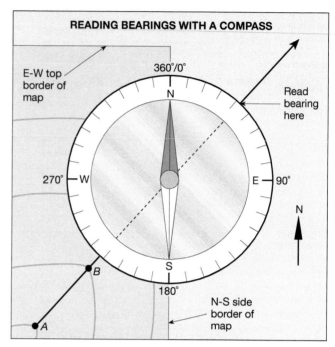

FIGURE 14 Examples of how to read the *bearing* (compass direction) from one point to another using a map and protractor (left) or compass (right). Remember that a compass points to Earth's *magnetic north pole* (MN) rather than the North Pole upon which the UTM and latitude-longitude grid of map is based, called *grid north* (GN). A diagram at the margin of each map shows the *declination* (difference) between MN and GN. If the MN arrow is to the right of GN then subtract the degrees of declination from your compass reading. If the MN arrow is to the left of GN then add the degrees of declination to your compass reading.

To determine a compass bearing on a map, draw a straight line from the starting point to the destination point and also through any one of the map's borders. For example, to find the bearing from **A** to **B**, a line was drawn through both points and the east edge of the map. Align a protractor (left drawing) or the N-S or E-W directional axis of a compass (right drawing) with the map's border and read the bearing in degrees toward the direction of the destination. For example above, notice that the *quadrant bearing* from point **A** to **B** is North 43° East (left map, using protractor) or an *azimuth bearing* of 43°. If you walked in the exact opposite direction, from **B** to **A**, then you would walk along a quadrant bearing of South 43° West or an azimuth bearing of 223° (i.e., 43° + 180° = 223°).

one at each corner of the property. The location of these rods is shown on the map in Figure 14 (left side) as points *A*, *B*, *C*, and *D*. The property deed notes the distances between the points *and* bearings between the points. This defines the shape of the property. Notice that the northwest edge of your property lies between two metal rods located at points *A* and *B*. You can measure the distance between the points using a tape measure. How can you measure the bearing?

First, draw a line (very lightly in pencil so that it can be erased) through the two points, *A* and *B*. Make sure the line also intersects an edge of the map. In both parts of Figure 14, a line was drawn through points *A* and *B* so that it also intersects the east edge of the map. Next, orient a protractor so that its 0° and 180° marks are on the edge of the map, with the 0°

end toward geographic north. Place the origin of the protractor at the point where your line *A*–*B* intersects the edge of the map. You can now read a bearing of 43° east of north. We express this as a quadrant bearing of "North 43° East" (written N43°E) or as an azimuth bearing of 43°. If you were to determine the opposite bearing, from *B* to *A*, then the bearing would be pointing southwest and would be read as "South 43° West," or as an azimuth of 223°.

You also can use a compass to read bearings, as shown in Figure 14 (right). Ignore the compass needle and use the compass as if it were a circular protractor. Some compasses are graduated in degrees, from 0–360, in which case you read an azimuth bearing from 0–360°. If GeoTools Sheets accompany your lab manual, square azimuth protractors are provided here.

Questions

1. Draw the 300-foot contour line on Figure 4. Draw the 1200-foot contour line on Darwin Volcano. Then use interpolation (Figure 6, rule 2) to draw the 600- and 900-foot contour lines on Darwin Volcano.

2. What are the latitude-longitude coordinates of point **B** in Figure 1?

3. What are the three forms of vegetation shown by the green patterns in sec. 29, T1N, R6W, in Figure 3?

4. The map in Figure 3 is contoured in feet above sea level. What is its contour interval?

5. Refer to Figure 3 and fill in the blanks below.

   a. The ratio scale of this map is: _____.

   b. One inch on this map equals exactly _____ inches in real life.

   c. One inch on this map equals exactly _____ mile(s) in real life, so we can say that 1 inch on the map equals approximately 1 mi on the ground.

6. Review how the location of point **x** in Figure 11C was determined using PLS shorthand (see the caption for Figure 11). Then, determine the location of point **z** in Figure 11C using PLS shorthand.

7. How many acres are present in the township in Figure 11B? (*Hint:* There are 640 acres in 1 mi².)

8. Imagine that you wanted to purchase the $NE\frac{1}{4}$ of the $SE\frac{1}{4}$ of section 11 in Figure 11C. If the property costs $500 per acre, then how much must you pay for the entire property? Explain.

9. Examine Figure 3.

   a. In what UTM Zone is this map located? Explain your reasoning.

   b. What are the exact UTM coordinates of the northeast corner of this map?

10. What is the bearing from point C to point D in Figure 14?

11. What is the bearing from point D to point C in Figure 14? (Refer to Figure 6 as needed.)

12. Most handheld 12-channel parallel GPS receivers have an error of about 15 m when they fix on their position, and most geologists plot their data on $7\frac{1}{2}$-minute topographic quadrangle maps that have a ratio scale of 1:24,000. If an object is 15 meters long in real life, then exactly how long (in millimeters) would it be on the 1:24,000 scale map?

13. Contour Figure 15 using a contour interval of 100 ft. (Refer to Figure 6 as needed.)

14. Contour Figure 16 using a contour interval of 10 ft. (Refer to Figure 6 as needed.)

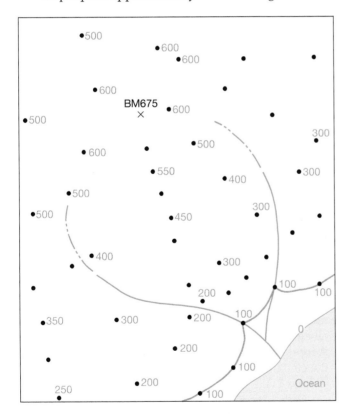

FIGURE 15 Use interpolation and extrapolation to estimate elevations of points that are not labeled (see Figure 6). Then add contour lines with a 100-foot contour interval. Note how the 0-foot and 100-foot contour lines have already been drawn.

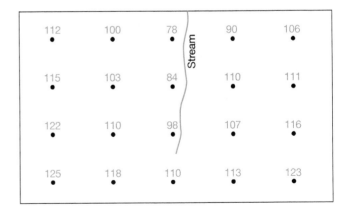

FIGURE 16 Construct a topographic map by contouring these elevations. Use a contour interval of 10 feet. (Refer to Figure 5 as needed.)

Contour Interval = 20 feet

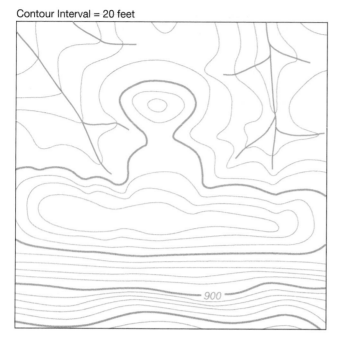

FIGURE 17   Topographic map interpretation. Use your pencil to lightly shade in the portion of this map that represents the highest elevation of land. Label a hill, "H." Label a ridge, "R." Label a saddle, "S." Use an arrow to label the lowest contour line in the map and label the arrow with the elevation of the contour. (Refer to Figures 5–8 as needed.)

Contour Interval = 20 feet

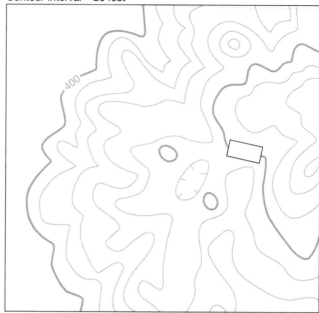

FIGURE 18   Topographic map interpretation. Use your pencil to lightly shade in the portion of this map that represents the lowest elevation. Label a closed depression, "CD." In the small box, write the elevation of the index contour on which it lies. (Refer to Figures 5–8 as needed.)

15. Using your pencil, color in the area of Figure 17 that represents the top of the highest hill.

16. In Figure 18, fill in the box on the index contour with its correct elevation in feet above sea level. (*Note:* Contour interval is 20 feet.) Using your pencil, color in the area of Figure 18 that represents the lowest elevations. Label a closed depression with the letters "CD."

17. Using a contour interval of 10 ft, label every contour line on the topographic map in Figure 19 with its exact elevation above sea level.

18. Analyze the topographic map in Figure 20.

    a. The contour lines on this map are labeled in meters. What is the contour interval of this map?

    b. What is the regional relief of the land represented in this map?

    c. What is the gradient from **Y** to **X**?

    d. How could you find the areas of this map that have a gradient of 20 meters per kilometer or greater? (*Hint:* Think of the contour interval and how many contour lines of map elevation must occur along one kilometer of map distance.)

    e. Imagine that you need to drive a truck from point **A** to point **B** in this mapped area and that your truck cannot travel up any slopes having a gradient over 20 m/km. Trace a route that you could drive to get from point **A** to point **B**. (More than one solution is possible.)

PART B: TOPOGRAPHIC PROFILES AND VERTICAL EXAGGERATION

A topographic map provides an overhead (aerial) view of an area, depicting features and relief by means of its symbols and contour lines. Occasionally a cross section of the topography is useful. A **topographic profile** is a cross section that shows the elevations and slopes along a given line (Figure 21).

Follow these steps and Figure 21 to construct a topographic profile:

Step 1: On the map, draw a **line of section** along which the profile is to be constructed. Label the section line **A**−**A'**. Be sure that the line intersects all of

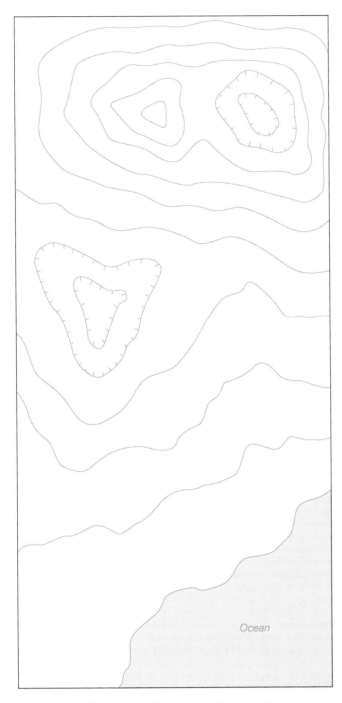

FIGURE 19 Complete this topographic map. Use a contour interval of 10 ft and label the elevation of every contour on the map. (*Hint*: Start at sea level and refer to Figures 8 and 9.)

the features (ridges, valleys, streams, etc.) that you wish the profile to show.

Step 2: On a strip of paper placed along section line **A–A′**, make tick marks at each place where a contour line intersects the section line and note the elevation

at the tick marks. Also note the location and elevation of points **A, A′**, and any streams crossed.

Step 3: Draw the profile. On a separate sheet of paper, draw a series of equally spaced parallel lines that are the same length as the line of section (graph paper can be used). Each horizontal line on this sheet represents a *constant elevation* and therefore corresponds to a contour line. The total number of horizontal lines that you need, and their elevations, depends on the total relief along the line of section and on whether you make the space between the lines equal to the contour interval, or to multiples of it (vertical exaggeration, which will be discussed shortly). Label your lines so that the highest and lowest elevations along the line of section will be within the grid.

Then, take the strip of paper you marked in Step 2 and place it along the base of your profile. Mark a dot on the grid above it for each elevation. Smoothly connect these dots to complete the topographic profile. (This line should not make angular bends. Make it a smoothly curving line that reflects the relief of the land surface along the line of section.)

Step 4: The vertical scale of your profile will vary greatly depending on how you draw the grid. It almost certainly will be larger than the horizontal scale of the map. This difference causes an exaggeration in the vertical dimension. Such exaggeration almost always is necessary to construct a readable profile, for without vertical exaggeration, the profile might be so shallow that only the highest peaks would be visible. Calculate the **vertical exaggeration** by one of two methods. *You can divide the horizontal ratio scale (1:24,000) by the vertical ratio scale (1:1,440)*, which reduces to 24,000/1,440, which reduces to 16.7 (Method 1, Step 4, Figure 21). Or *you can divide the vertical fractional scale (1/1,440) by the horizontal fractional scale (1/24,000)*, which reduces to 24,000/1,440, which reduces to 16.7 (Method 2, Step 4, Figure 21). The number 16.7 (usually written 16.7 ×) indicates that the relief shown on the profile is 16.7 times greater than the true relief. This makes the slopes on the profile 16.7 times steeper than the corresponding real slopes on the ground.

Question

19. In Figure 22, construct a topographic profile (using the graph paper provided beneath it) and calculate its vertical exaggeration.

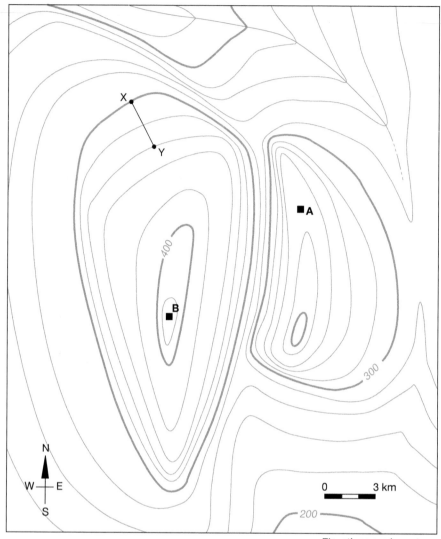

Elevations are in meters.

FIGURE 20 *Gradient* is a measure of the steepness of a slope, expressed in feet per mile or meters per kilometer. To determine the gradient of a slope, divide the *relief* (difference in elevation between two points on a map) by the distance measured between the two points. This is sometimes called *rise over run*. For example, this topographic map is contoured in meters. Can you determine the contour interval? Can you determine the gradient from point **X** to point **Y**? Can you plot a path from point **A** to point **B** that does not cross any slopes with a gradient above 20 meters per kilometer? Explain your reasoning.

Step 1

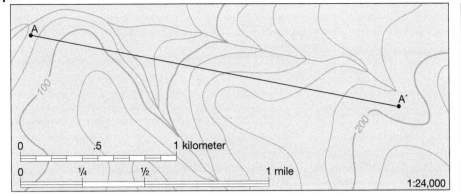

0   .5   1 kilometer

0   1/4   1/2   1 mile

1:24,000

Step 2

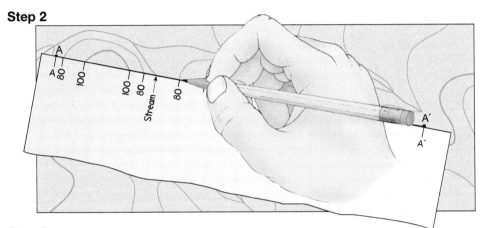

Step 3

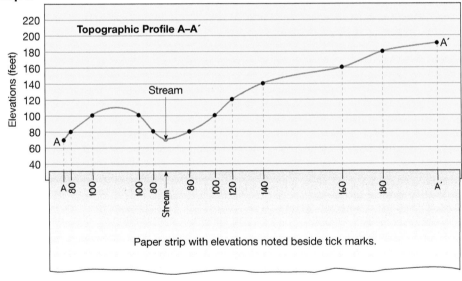

Paper strip with elevations noted beside tick marks.

Step 4 Vertical Exaggeration

On most topographic profiles, the vertical scale is exaggerated (stretched) to make landscape features more obvious. One must calculate how much the vertical scale (V) has been exaggerated in comparison to the horizontal scale (H).

The horizontal scale is the map's scale. This map has an H ratio scale of 1:24,000, which means that 1 inch on the map equals 24,000 inches of real elevation. It is the same as a H fractional scale of 1/24,000.

On the vertical scale of this topographic profile, one inch equals 120 feet or 1,440 inches (120 feet x 12 inches/foot). Since one inch on the vertical scale equals 1,440 inches of real elevation, the topographic profile has a V ratio scale of 1:1,440 and a V fractional scale of 1/1,440.

The vertical exaggeration of this topographic profile is calculated by either method below:

Method 1: Divide the horizontal ratio scale by the vertical ratio scale.

$$\frac{\text{H ratio scale}}{\text{V ratio scale}} = \frac{1{:}24{,}000}{1{:}1{,}440} = \frac{24{,}000}{1{,}440} = 16.7\times$$

Method 2: Divide the vertical fractional scale by the horizontal fractional scale.

$$\frac{\text{V fractional scale}}{\text{H fractional scale}} = \frac{1/1{,}440}{1/24{,}000} = \frac{24{,}000}{1{,}440} = 16.7\times$$

FIGURE 21 Topographic profile construction and vertical exaggeration. Shown are a topographic map (Step 1), topographic profile constructed along line **A−A′** (Steps 2 and 3), and calculation of vertical exaggeration (Step 4). **Step 1**—Select two points (**A, A′**), and the line between them (line **A−A′**), along which you want to construct a topographic profile. **Step 2**—To construct the profile, the edge of a strip of paper was placed along line **A−A′** on the topographic map. A tick mark was then placed on the edge of the paper at each point where a contour line and stream intersected the edge of the paper. The elevation represented by each contour line was noted on its corresponding tick mark. **Step 3**—The edge of the strip of paper (with tick marks and elevations) was placed along the bottom line of a piece of lined paper, and the lined paper was graduated for elevations (along its right margin). A black dot was placed on the profile above each tick mark at the elevation noted on the tick mark. The black dots were then connected with a smooth line to complete the topographic profile. **Step 4**—*Vertical exaggeration* of the profile was calculated using either of two methods. Thus, the vertical dimension of this profile is exaggerated (stretched) to 16.7 times greater than it actually appears in nature compared to the horizontal/map dimension.

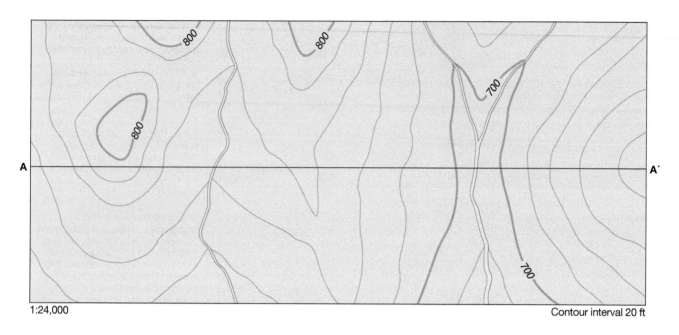

1:24,000

Contour interval 20 ft

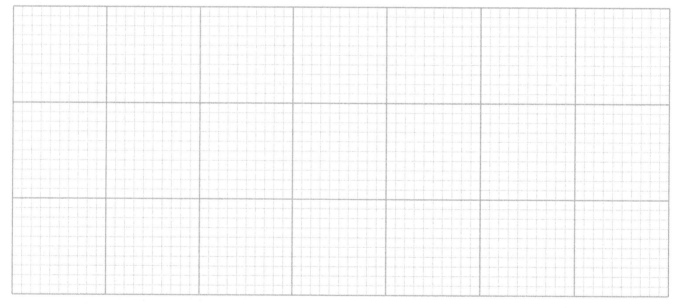

FIGURE 22 Topographic profile construction and vertical exaggeration. Can you construct a topographic profile for line **A–A'** and calculate its vertical exaggeration?

PART C: ANALYSIS OF THE ONTARIO, CALIFORNIA, TOPOGRAPHIC MAP

Questions

Refer to Figure 3 to answer the following questions.

20. What natural feature is located in the $SW\frac{1}{4}$, $NE\frac{1}{4}$, sec. 13, T1N, R7W? (*Hint:* It is a small body of water.)

21. Locate Bighorn Peak in the northwest corner of the map.

a. Use the PLS numbering system to describe the location of Bighorn Peak.

b. Use UTM coordinates to describe the location of Bighorn Peak.

c. What is the exact elevation of Bighorn Peak?

22. What is the distance in kilometers from the railroad intersection in Grapeland (sec. 31, T1N,

R6W) to the Day Canyon Guard Station (sec. 17, T1N, R6W)?

23. What is the difference in elevation between Grapeland and the Day Canyon Guard Station?

24. What is the average gradient of the land between Grapeland and the Day Canyon Guard Station?

25. In what general direction does the stream in Day Canyon flow (sec. 31, T2N, R6W and sec. 6, T1N, R6W)? How can you tell?

26. What is the total relief on this map area? Show your calculation.

PART D: ANALYSIS OF YOUR TOPOGRAPHIC QUADRANGLE MAP

Questions

Refer to the quadrangle map provided by your instructor (or otherwise obtained by you) and answer the following questions. (*Do not mark the map with any dark lines or pen marks!*)

27. What latitude line marks the northern boundary of the quadrangle?

28. What latitude line marks the southern boundary of the quadrangle?

29. What longitude line marks the eastern boundary of the quadrangle?

30. What longitude line marks the western boundary of the quadrangle?

31. What is the distance (in degrees, minutes, and seconds) from the southern to the northern boundary of the quadrangle?

32. What is the distance (in degrees, minutes, and seconds) from the western to the eastern boundary of the quadrangle?

33. Is this a $7\frac{1}{2}$-minute quadrangle or a 15-minute quadrangle?

34. What UTM datum(s) is/are represented on the map?

35. In what UTM Zone is this map located?

36. Give the location of the northwest corner of the map in UTM coordinates. Be sure to specify the datum used if there is more than one datum represented on the map.

37. What is the magnetic declination (between true north and magnetic north) of this quadrangle?

38. In what year was the map originally published?

39. What is the fractional scale of this quadrangle?

40. How can this scale be expressed as a verbal scale in miles? In kilometers?

41. Two inches on this quadrangle map represent how many feet on the ground? How many miles? How many kilometers?

42. What is the name of this quadrangle?

43. What is the name of the quadrangle map directly adjacent to the south?

44. What color was used to indicate these features?

   a. water

   b. vegetation (mainly woods or forests)

   c. contour lines

   d. buildings

45. Was this map ever photorevised? If so, when?

46. What is the elevation of the highest point on the quadrangle?

47. What is the elevation of the lowest point on the quadrangle?

48. What is the total relief within the quadrangle?

PART E: AERIAL PHOTOGRAPHS

Aerial photographs are pictures of Earth taken from airplanes, with large cameras that generally make 9-by-9-inch negatives. Most of these photographs are black and white, but color pictures sometimes are available. The photographs may be large scale or small scale, depending on the elevation at which they were taken, on the focal length of the camera lens, and on whether the pictures have been enlarged or reduced from the negatives.

Air photographs can be taken nearly straight down from the plane, termed *vertical*, or they may be taken at an angle to the vertical, termed *oblique*. Oblique views help reveal geological features and landforms; however, vertical air photographs are even more useful in geological studies. The photographs used in this exercise are verticals.

Vertical air photos are taken in a series during a flight so that the images form a continuous view of the area below. They are taken so that approximately 60% image overlap occurs between any two adjacent photos. The view is straight down at the very center of each picture (called the *center point* or *principal point*), but all other portions of the landscape are viewed at an angle that becomes increasingly oblique away from the center of the picture.

The scale of any photographic image cannot be uniform, because it differs with the distance of the camera lens from the ground. Thus, in photos of flat terrain, the scale is largest at the center of the photo, where the ground is closest to the camera lens, and decreases away from the center. Also, hilltops and other high points that are closer to the camera lens are shown at larger scales than are valley bottoms and other low places.

Air photos commonly are overlapped to form a **stereogram,** or **stereo pair,** to be viewed with a *stereoscope* (Figures 23, 24). When the photos are viewed through the stereoscope, the image appears three-dimensional (stereo). This view is startling, dramatic, and reveals surprises about the terrain, as you shall see shortly. Stereoscopes can be of many types, but the most commonly used variety is a *pocket stereoscope* such as the one shown in Figure 23.

Figure 24 shows parts of three overlapping vertical air photos. They have been cropped (trimmed) and mounted in sequence. The view is of Garibaldi Provincial Park in British Columbia, Canada. All three pictures show a dark volcanic cinder cone bulging out into Garibaldi Lake from the edge of Mount Price. Each photo shows it from a different overhead viewpoint. These landscape features are depicted by contours on the topographic map in Figure 25.

The center point of each photo is marked with a circled **X.** In the right-hand photo (BC 866:50), the center point is in the lake. In the middle photo (BC 866:49), it is near the cinder cone. In the left-hand photo (BC 866:48), it is near the margin of the page. By locating these center points on the map and connecting them with straight lines, you can see the **flight line,** or route flown by the photographing aircraft.

Locating the centers of these photos on the topographic map (Figure 25) is not easy, because the map and the photos show different types of features. However, you can plot the centers fairly accurately by referring to recognizable topographic features such as stream valleys and angles in the lakeshore.

Questions

49. Notice how the image of the cinder cone is distorted when you compare the three successive pictures. Not only is the base of the cone different in each picture, but the round patch of snow in the central crater appears to shift position relative to the base. In which photograph (left, middle, or right) does the image of the cone appear to be least

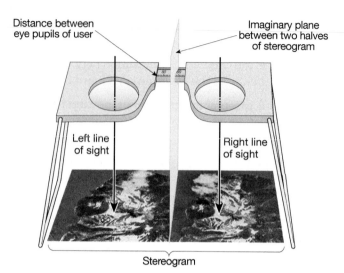

FIGURE 23 How to use a pocket stereoscope. First, have a partner measure the distance between the pupils of your eyes, in millimeters. Set the distance on the stereoscope. Then, position the stereoscope so that your lines of sight are aimed at a common point on each half of the stereogram (stereopair). As you look through the stereoscope, move it around slightly until the image "pops" into three dimensions. Be patient during this first attempt so that your eyes can focus correctly.

Most people do not need a stereoscope to see the stereograms in stereo (three-dimensions). Try holding the stereogram at a comfortable distance (one foot or so) from your eyes. Cross your eyes until you see four photographs (two stereograms), then relax your eyes to let the two center photographs merge into one stereo image.

distorted? Why? The same varying-perspective view that distorts features in air photos also makes it possible to view them **stereoscopically.** Thus, when any two overlapping photos in a sequence are placed side-by-side and viewed with the stereoscope, you see the overlap area as a vertically exaggerated three-dimensional image of the landscape. (With practice, you can train your eyes to do this without a stereoscope.)

50. The scale of the original negatives of the Garibaldi Lake photos is approximately 1:31,680, or 1 inch $= \frac{1}{2}$ mile. However, the pictures reproduced here have been reduced in size. Calculate their scale by measuring corresponding distances on the photos and on the topographic map, setting these distances as a ratio, and then multiplying the map scale by this ratio. What is the nominal scale thus derived? (You must write "nominal scale" because the actual scale differs with elevation and distance from the camera lens, as mentioned above.)

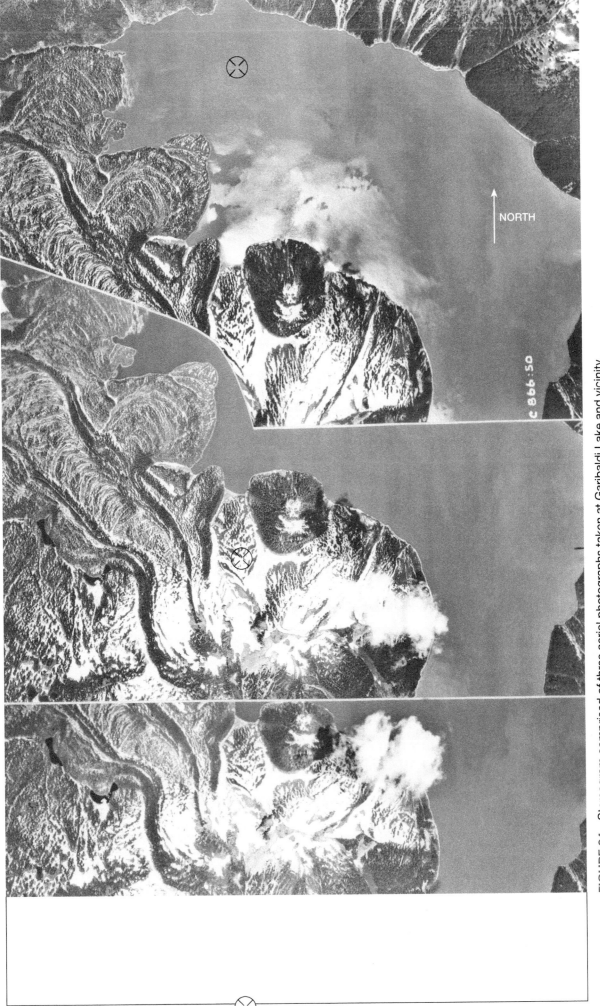

FIGURE 24 Stereogram comprised of three aerial photographs taken at Garibaldi Lake and vicinity, British Columbia, on 13 July 1949. (Photos BC 866:48–50, reproduced courtesy of Surveys & Resource Mapping Branch, Ministry of Environment, Government of British Columbia, Canada.)

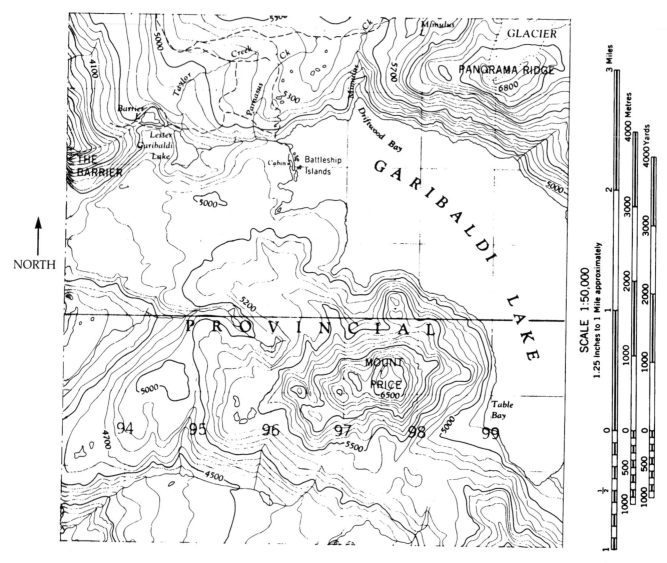

FIGURE 25 Portion of the Cheakamus River, East, topographic quadrangle map, British Columbia, on 13 July 1949; the same time at which the stereogram in Figure 24 was made. (Reproduced courtesy of Surveys & Resource Mapping Branch, Ministry of Environment, Government of British Columbia, Canada.)

51. Photograph BC 866:48 shows two broad pathways that sweep down the slopes of Mount Price from a point near the summit. One trends down to the south and west and the other to the north and west. Both are bordered by narrow ridges. What are these features? Of what rock type are they probably formed?

52. On the map and stereogram, examine both sides of the outlet channel where Garibaldi Lake over-

flows into Lesser Garibaldi Lake, near the northwest corner of BC 866:50. Is the rock that forms the slopes on the north side of the outlet channel the same or different from that on the south side? Name two features in the photos that lead you to this interpretation.

53. Lakes, and the basins they occupy, can be formed in many ways. On the basis of these photos, how do you think Garibaldi Lake formed?

Stream Processes, Landscapes, Mass Wastage, and Flood Hazards

---

•CONTRIBUTING AUTHORS•

Pamela J.W. Gore • *Georgia Perimeter College*

Richard W. Macomber • *Long Island University–Brooklyn*

Cherukupalli E. Nehru • *Brooklyn College (CUNY)*

OBJECTIVES

A. Be able to use topographic maps and stereograms to describe and interpret streams: their valley shapes, channel configurations, drainage patterns, and the erosional landscapes and depositional features they create.

B. Understand erosional and mass wastage processes that occur at Niagara Falls, and be able to evaluate rates at which the falls is retreating upstream.

C. Explore and infer meander evolution on the Rio Grande.

D. Be able to construct a flood magnitude/frequency graph, map flooded and flood hazard zones, and assess the extent of flood hazards along the Flint River, Georgia.

E. Be able to determine the flood hazard level where you live and what to do if you are caught in a flood (using online resources of the Federal Emergency Management Agency).

MATERIALS

Pencil, eraser, laboratory notebook, ruler, calculator, 12-inch length of string, pocket stereoscope (optional), and highlighter pen (optional for Question 6).

INTRODUCTION

It all starts with a single raindrop, then another and another. As water drenches the landscape, some soaks into the ground and becomes *groundwater*. Some flows over the ground and into streams and ponds of *surface water*. The streams will continue to flow for as long as they receive a water supply from additional rain, melting snow, or *base flow* (groundwater that seeps into a stream via porous rocks, fractures, and springs).

Perennial streams flow continuously throughout the year and are represented on topographic maps as blue lines. *Intermittent streams* flow only at certain times of the year, such as rainy seasons or when snow melts in the Spring. They are represented on topographic maps as blue line segments separated by blue dots (three blue dots between each line segment). All streams, perennial and intermittent, have the potential to **flood** (overflow their banks). Floods damage more human property in the United States than any other natural hazard.

Streams are also the single most important natural agent of *land erosion* (wearing away of the land). They erode more sediment from the land than wind, glaciers, or ocean waves. The sediment is transported and eventually deposited, whereupon it is called **alluvium**. Alluvium consists of gravel, sand, silt, and clay deposited in floodplains,

---

point bars, channel bars, deltas, and alluvial fans (Figure 1).

Therefore, stream processes (or *fluvial processes*) are among the most important agents that shape Earth's surface and cause damage to humans and their property.

PART A: STREAM PROCESSES AND LANDSCAPES

Recall the last time you experienced a drenching rainstorm. Where did all the water go? During drenching rainstorms, some of the water seeps slowly into the ground. But most of the water flows over the ground before it can seep in. It flows over fields, streets, and sidewalks as sheets of water several millimeters or centimeters deep. This is called *sheet flow.*

Sheet flow moves downslope in response to the pull of gravity, so the sheets of water flow from streets and sidewalks to ditches and street gutters. From the ditches and storm sewers, it flows downhill into small streams. Small streams merge to form larger streams, larger streams merge to form rivers, and rivers flow into lakes and oceans. This entire drainage network, from the smallest *upland* tributaries to larger streams, to the largest river (*main stream* or *main river*), is called a **stream drainage system** (Figure 1A).

Stream Drainage Patterns

Stream drainage systems form characteristic patterns of drainage, depending on the relief and geology of the land. The common patterns below are illustrated in Figure 2:

- **Dendritic pattern**—resembles the branching of a tree. Water flow is from the branch-like tributaries to the trunk-like main stream or river. This pattern is common where a stream cuts into flat lying layers of rock or sediment. It also develops where a stream cuts into homogeneous rock (crystalline igneous rock) or sediment (sand).

- **Rectangular pattern**—a network of channels with right-angle bends that form a pattern of interconnected rectangles and squares. This pattern often develops over rocks that are fractured or faulted in two main directions that are perpendicular (at nearly right angles) and break the bedrock into rectangular or square blocks. The streams erode channels along the perpendicular fractures and faults.

- **Radial pattern**—channel flow outward from a central area, resembling the spokes of a wheel. Water drains from the inside of the pattern, where

the "spokes" nearly meet, to the outside of the pattern (where the "spokes" are farthest apart). This pattern develops on conical hills, such as volcanoes and some structural domes.

- **Centripetal pattern**—channels converge on a central point, often a lake or playa (dry lake bed), at the center of a closed basin (a basin from which surface water cannot drain because there is no outlet valley).

- **Annular pattern**—a set of incomplete, concentric rings of streams connected by short radial channels. This pattern commonly develops on eroding structural domes and folds that contain alternating folded layers of resistant and nonresistant rock types.

- **Trellis pattern**—resembles a vine or climbing rose bush growing on a trellis, where the main stream is long and intersected at nearly right angles by its tributaries. This pattern commonly develops where alternating layers of resistant and nonresistant rocks have been tilted and eroded to form a series of parallel ridges and valleys. The main stream channel cuts through the ridges, and the main tributaries flow perpendicular to the main stream and along the valleys (parallel to and between the ridges).

- **Deranged pattern**—a random pattern of stream channels that seem to have no relationship to underlying rock types or geologic structures.

Drainage Basins and Divides

The entire area of land that is drained by one stream, or an entire stream drainage system, is called a **drainage basin.** And the linear boundaries that separate one drainage basin from another are called **divides.**

Some divides are easy to recognize on maps as knife-edge ridge crests. However, in regions of lower relief or rolling hills, the divides separate one gentle slope from another and are more difficult to locate precisely (Figure 1A, dashed line surrounding the Tributary X drainage basin). For this reason, divides cannot always be mapped as distinct lines. In the absence of detailed elevation data, they must be represented by dashed lines that signify their most probable locations.

You may have heard of something called a *continental divide,* which is a narrow strip of land dividing surface waters that drain in opposite directions across the continent (Figure 3). The continental divide in North America is an imaginary line along the crest of the Rocky Mountains. Rainwater that falls

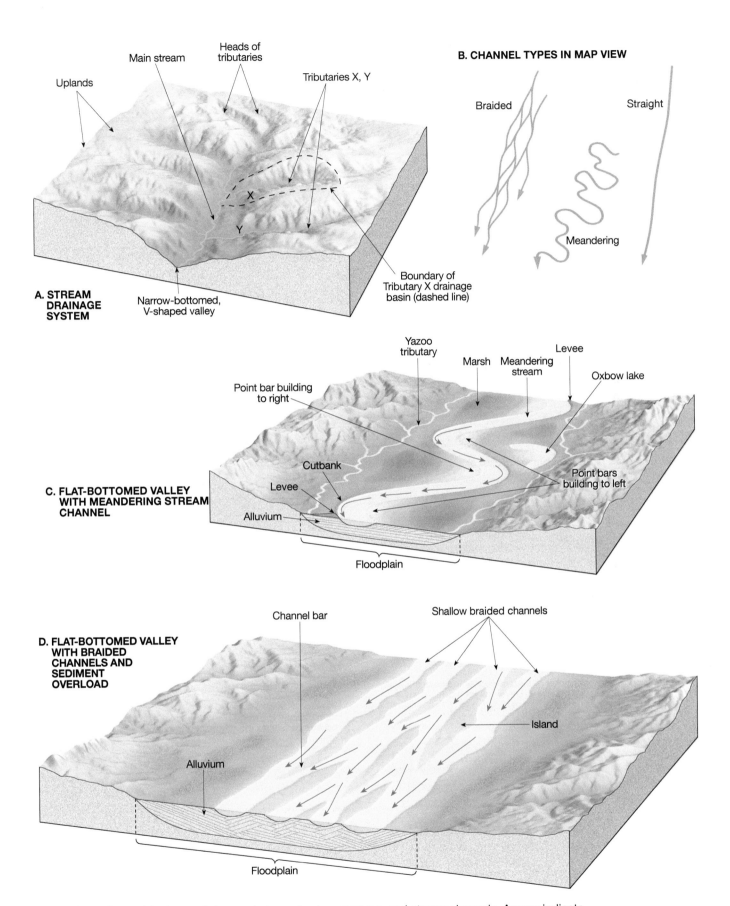

FIGURE 1 General features of stream drainage basins, streams, and stream channels. Arrows indicate current flow in main stream channels. **A.** Features of a stream drainage basin. **B.** Stream channel types as observed in map view. **C.** Features of a meandering stream valley. **D.** Features of a typical braided stream. Braided streams develop in sediment-choked streams.

STREAM DRAINAGE PATTERNS

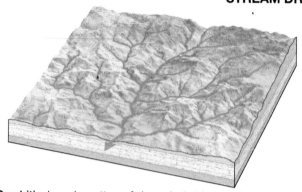

Dendritic: Irregular pattern of channels that branch like a tree. Develops on flat lying or homogeneous rock.

Rectangular: Channels have right-angle bends developed along perpendicular sets of rock fractures or joints.

Radial: Channels radiate outward like spokes of a wheel from a high point.

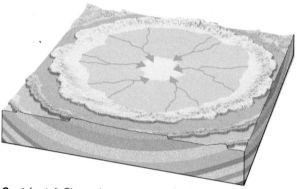

Centripetal: Channels converge on the lowest point in a closed basin from which water cannot drain.

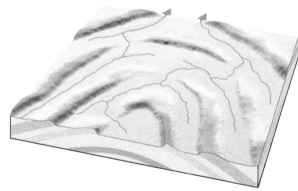

Annular: Long channels form a pattern of concentric circles connected by short radial channels. Develops on eroded domes or folds with resistant and nonresistant rock types.

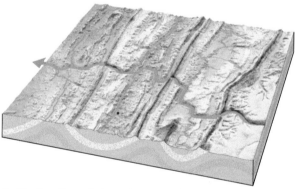

Trellis: A pattern of channels resembling a vine growing on a trellis. Develops where tilted layers of resistant and nonresistant rock form parallel ridges and valleys. The main stream channel cuts through the ridges, and the main tributaries flow along the valleys parallel to the ridges and at right angles to the main stream.

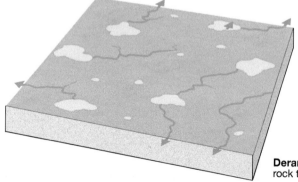

Deranged: Channels flow randomly with no relation to underlying rock types or structures.

FIGURE 2 Some stream drainage patterns and their relationship to bedrock geology.

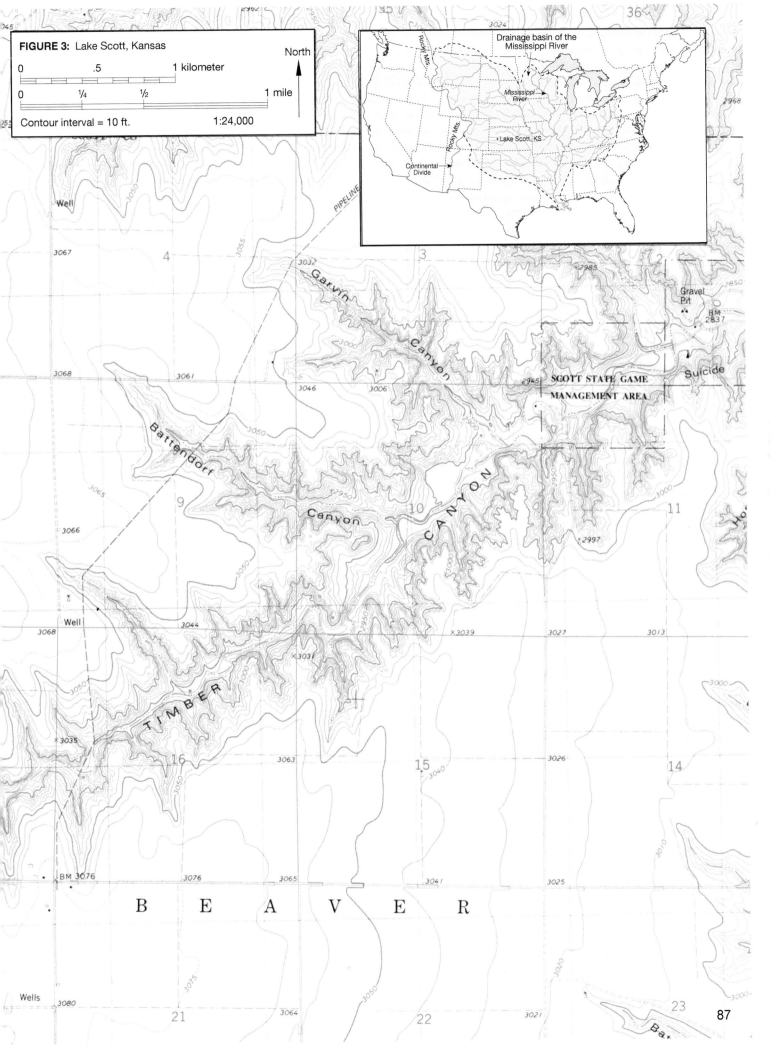

FIGURE 3: Lake Scott, Kansas

North

0 .5 1 kilometer

0 ¼ ½ 1 mile

Contour interval = 10 ft.　　　　1:24,000

Drainage basin of the
Mississippi River

Rocky Mts.

Mississippi
River

Rocky Mts.

Lake Scott, KS

Continental
Divide

PIPELINE

Garvin Canyon

Battendorf Canyon

CANYON

SCOTT STATE GAME
MANAGEMENT AREA

Gravel
Pit

BM
2837

Suicide

Well

Well

Wells

TIMBER

B E A V E R

BM 3076

87

east of the line drains eastward into the Atlantic Ocean, and rainwater that falls west of the line drains westward into the Pacific Ocean. Therefore, North America's continental divide is sometimes called "The Great Divide."

Stream Weathering, Transportation, and Deposition

Three main processes are at work in every stream. *Weathering* occurs where the stream physically erodes and disintegrates Earth materials and where it chemically decomposes or dissolves Earth materials to form sediment and aqueous chemical solutions. *Transportation* of these weathered materials occurs when they are dragged, bounced, and carried downstream (as suspended grains or chemicals in the water). *Deposition* occurs if the velocity of the stream drops (allowing sediments to settle out of the water) or if parts of the stream evaporate (allowing mineral crystals and oxide residues to form).

The smallest valleys in a drainage basin occur at its highest elevations, called **uplands** (Figure 1). In the uplands, a stream's (tributary's) point of origin, or **head,** may be at a spring or at the start of narrow runoff channels developed during rainstorms. Erosion (wearing away rock and sediment) is the dominant process here, and the stream channels deepen and erode their V-shaped channels uphill through time—a process called **headward erosion.** Eroded sediment is transported downstream by the tributaries.

Streams also weather and erode their own valleys along weaknesses in the rocks (fractures, faults), soluble nonresistant layers of rock (salt layers, limestone), and where there is the least resistance to erosion (see Figure 2). Rocks comprised of hard, chemically resistant minerals are generally more resistant to erosion and form ridges or other hilltops. Rocks comprised of soft and more easily weathered minerals are generally less resistant to erosion and form valleys. This is commonly called *differential erosion* of rock.

Headward tributary valleys merge into larger stream valleys, and these eventually merge into a larger river valley. Along the way, some new materials are eroded, and deposits (gravel, sand, mud) may form temporarily, but the main processes at work over the years in uplands are erosion (headward erosion and cutting V-shaped valleys) and transportation of sediment.

The end of a river valley is the **mouth** of the river, where it enters a lake, ocean, or dry basin. At this location, the river water is dispersed into a wider area, its velocity decreases, and sediment settles out of suspension to form an alluvial deposit (alluvial fan or delta). If the river water enters a dry basin, then it will evaporate and precipitate layers of mineral crystals and oxide residues (in a *playa*).

River Valley Forms and Processes

The form or shape of a river valley varies with these main factors:

- **Geology**—the bedrock geology over which the stream flows affects the stream's ability to find or erode its course (Figure 2).

- **Gradient**—the steepness of a slope—either the slope of a valley wall or the slope of a stream along a selected length (segment) of its channel (Figure 4). Gradient is generally expressed in *feet per mile.* This is determined by dividing the vertical rise or fall between two points on the slope (in feet) by the horizontal distance (run) between them (in miles). For example, if a stream descends 20 feet over a distance of 40 miles, then its gradient is 20 ft/40 mi, or 0.5 ft/mi. You can estimate the gradient of a stream by studying the spacing of contours on a topographic map. Or, you can precisely calculate the exact gradient by measuring how much a stream descends along a measured segment of its course.

- **Base level**—the lowest level to which a stream can theoretically erode. For example, base level is achieved where a stream enters a lake or ocean. At that point, the erosional (cutting) power of the stream is zero and depositional (sediment accumulation) processes occur.

- **Discharge**—the rate of stream flow at a given time and location. Discharge is measured in water volume per unit of time, commonly *cubic feet per second* (ft^3/sec).

- **Load**—the amount of material (mostly alluvium, but also plants, trash, and dissolved material) that is transported by a stream. In the uplands, most streams have relatively steep gradients, so the streams cut narrow, V-shaped valleys. Near their heads, tributaries are quick to transport their load downstream, where it combines with the loads of other tributaries. Therefore, the load of the tributaries is transferred to the larger streams and, eventually, to the main river. The load is eventually deposited at the mouth of the river, where it enters a lake, ocean, or dry basin.

From the headwaters to the mouth of a stream, the gradient decreases, discharge increases, and

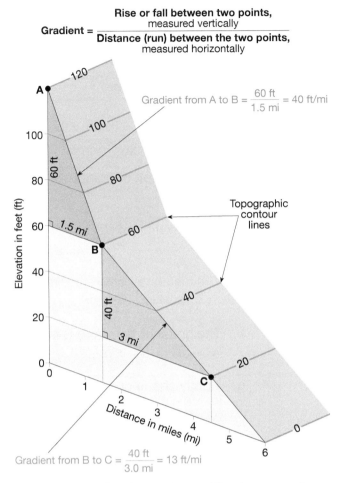

$$\text{Gradient} = \frac{\text{Rise or fall between two points, measured vertically}}{\text{Distance (run) between the two points, measured horizontally}}$$

Gradient from A to B = $\frac{60 \text{ ft}}{1.5 \text{ mi}}$ = 40 ft/mi

Topographic contour lines

Gradient from B to C = $\frac{40 \text{ ft}}{3.0 \text{ mi}}$ = 13 ft/mi

FIGURE 4 **Gradient** is a measure of the steepness of a slope. As above, gradient is usually determined by dividing the rise or fall (vertical relief) between two points on the map by the distance (run) between them. It is usually expressed as a fraction in feet per mile (as above) or meters per kilometer.

A second way to determine and express the gradient of a slope is by measuring its steepness in degrees relative to horizontal. Thirdly, gradient can be expressed as a percentage (also called *grade* of a slope). For example, a grade of 10% would mean a grade of 10 units of rise divided by (per) 100 units of distance (i.e., 10 in. per 100 in., 10 m per 100 m).

valleys generally widen. Along the way, the load of the stream may exceed the ability of the water to carry it, so the solid particles accumulate as sedimentary deposits along the river margins, or banks. **Floodplains** develop when alluvium accumulates landward of the river banks, during floods (Figures 1C and 1D). However, most flooding events do not submerge the entire floodplain. The more abundant minor flooding events deposit sediment only where the water barely overflows the river's banks. Over time, this creates natural **levees** (Figure 1C) that are higher than the rest of the flood-plain. If a tributary cannot breach a river's levee, then it will become a **yazoo tributary** that flows parallel to the river (Figure 1C).

Still farther downstream, the gradient decreases even more as discharge and load increase. The stream valleys develop very wide, flat floodplains with sinuous channels. These channels may become highly sinuous, or **meandering** (see Figures 1B and 1C). Erosion occurs on the outer edge of meanders, which are called **cutbanks.** At the same time, **point bar** deposits (mostly gravel and sand) accumulate along the inner edge of meanders. Progressive erosion of cutbanks and deposition of point bars makes meanders "migrate" over time.

Channels may cut new paths during floods. This can cut off the outer edge of a meander, abandoning it to become a crescent-shaped **oxbow lake** (see Figure 1C). When low gradient/high discharge streams become overloaded with sediment, they may form **braided stream** patterns. These consist of braided channels with linear, underwater sandbars (**channel bars**) and islands (see Figures 1B and 1D).

Some stream valleys have level surfaces that are higher than the present floodplain. These are remnants of older floodplains that have been dissected (cut by younger streams) and are called **stream terraces.** Sometimes several levels of stream terraces may be developed along a stream, resembling steps.

Where a stream enters a lake, ocean, or dry basin, its velocity decreases dramatically. The stream drops its sediment load, which accumulates as a triangular or fan-shaped deposit. In a lake or ocean, such a deposit is called a **delta.** A similar fan-shaped deposit of stream sediment also occurs where a steep-gradient stream abruptly enters a wide, level plain, creating an **alluvial fan.**

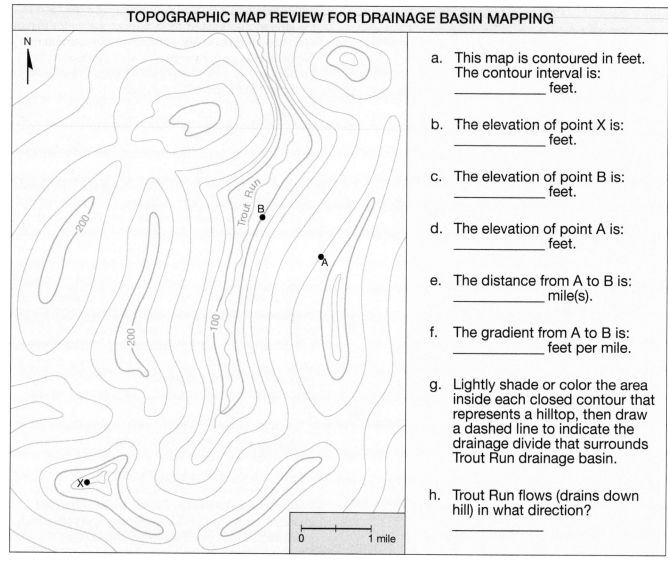

FIGURE 5 Topographic map for analysis and interpretation in Question 1.

Questions

1. Refer to Figure 5 and complete items **a** through **h.**

2. Imagine that drums of oil were emptied (illegally) at location **X** in Figure 5. Is it likely that the oil would eventually wash downhill into Trout Run? Explain your reasoning.

3. Refer to the topographic map of the Lake Scott quadrangle, Kansas (Figure 3).

   a. Draw and label a dashed line on this map that is the divide between Battendorf Canyon (NE $\frac{1}{4}$ sec. 9) and the smaller canyon that runs from the SW $\frac{1}{4}$ sec. 9 to the "B" in the word "TIMBER" ($\frac{1}{2}$ mile north of the center of sec. 16).

   b. Draw and label a dashed line at the boundary of the Garvin Canyon drainage basin.

4. Notice that the upland surface of the Lake Scott, Kansas, quadrangle (see Figure 3) is not horizontal.

   a. In what general direction does water flow over the upland surface?

   b. What is the gradient of this upland surface? (Show your mathematical calculation.)

   c. The mudstone bedrock of these uplands is overlain by alluvium (sand and gravel) that was deposited about 10,000–12,000 years ago by streams draining from melting glaciers (prior to dissection of the surface as it appears today). It is the upper surface of this alluvium that has the attitude described in **a** and **b,** above. What is the probable source area for the water and sediments that formed this alluvial deposit? Explain your reasoning. (*Hint:* Notice at the top of Figure 3 that this area is just east of the Great Divide.)

5. Reconsider the uplands and upland alluvium discussed in Question 4. The extensive sheet of upland alluvium was probably deposited by braided streams (see Figures 1B and 1D) in an older stage of landscape development.

   a. What drainage pattern (shown in Figure 2) currently is developed in this area?

   b. What does this modern drainage pattern suggest about the attitude of bedrock layers (the mudstone layers beneath the upland alluvium) in this area (refer to Figure 2)? Explain your reasoning.

6. Examine the landscape of the Waldron, Arkansas, quadrangle (Figure 6). What drainage pattern is developed in this area, and what does it suggest about the attitude of bedrock layers on this area? Explain your reasoning. (*Hint:* Refer to Figure 2. It may also be useful to trace the linear hilltops with a highlighter so you can see their orientation relative to streams.)

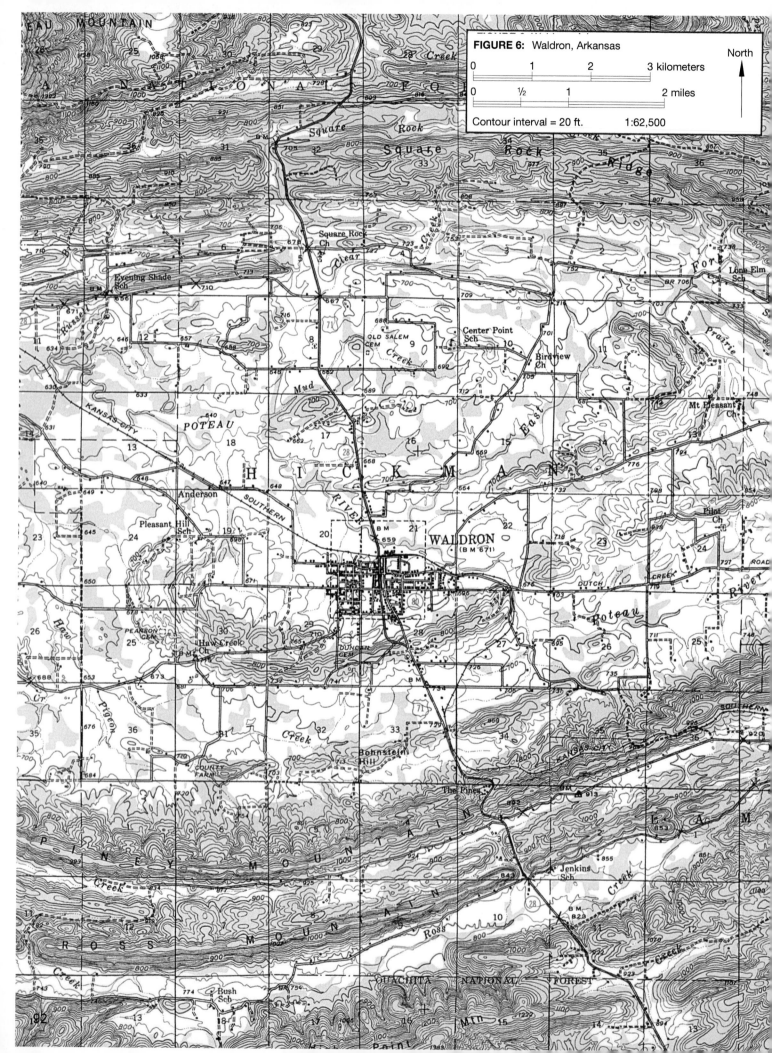

FIGURE 6: Waldron, Arkansas

Contour interval = 20 ft.   1:62,500

PART B: STREAM PROCESSES AND LANDSCAPES NEAR VOLTAIRE, NORTH DAKOTA

Refer to the Voltaire, North Dakota, quadrangle (Figure 7) and stereogram (Figure 8).

Questions

7. Glaciers (composed of a mixture of ice, gravel, sand, and mud) were present in this region at the end of the Pleistocene Ice Age. When the glaciers melted about 11,000–12,000 years ago, a thick layer of sand and gravel was deposited on top of the bedrock, and streams began forming from the glacial meltwater. Therefore, streams have been eroding and shaping this landscape for about 11,000–12,000 years. Notice how well-developed the meanders and floodplains of the Souris River are. The landscape around Lake Scott, Kansas (Figure 3), is about the same age (i.e., 10,000–12,000 years old). Explain why you think there are such differences in forms of the valleys and types of stream channels between the Voltaire region and the Lake Scott region.

8. On Figures 7 and 8, note the swampy oxbow lakes and depressions (hachured contours on Figure 7) in the Souris River floodplain. These show that the river channel has changed course repeatedly. Explain how its course has changed at the oxbow just east of Westgaard Cemetery (see northeast of map center, NE $\frac{1}{4}$ sect. 3, Figure 7).

9. Do the hachured contours and other oxbows of the Souris River Valley show that this same process has occurred elsewhere along the valley? If so, then suggest one location.

10. What is one location along the course of the Souris River where the same thing may happen in the future if the course of the channel is not controlled by engineers?

11. Imagine what the topographic profile looks like along **X–X'**. (Refer to the stereogram in Figure 8 to help you with this.) Notice the relatively flat areas of the profile, such as those in SW $\frac{1}{4}$ sec. 33 and SE $\frac{1}{4}$ sec. 4 (Figure 7).

   a. What are these features called?

   b. How did they form?

   c. How could vegetation be used to map the location of the modern floodplain?

12. In SE $\frac{1}{4}$ sec. 3 (Figure 7), a stream trends northeast–southeast. What is the name of this type of stream and how did it probably form?

13. Notice the marsh in sec. 9 (Figure 7) and the depression on which it is located. What was this depression before it became a marsh?

14. How might the discharge of the Souris River have changed over the past 12,000 years? Why?

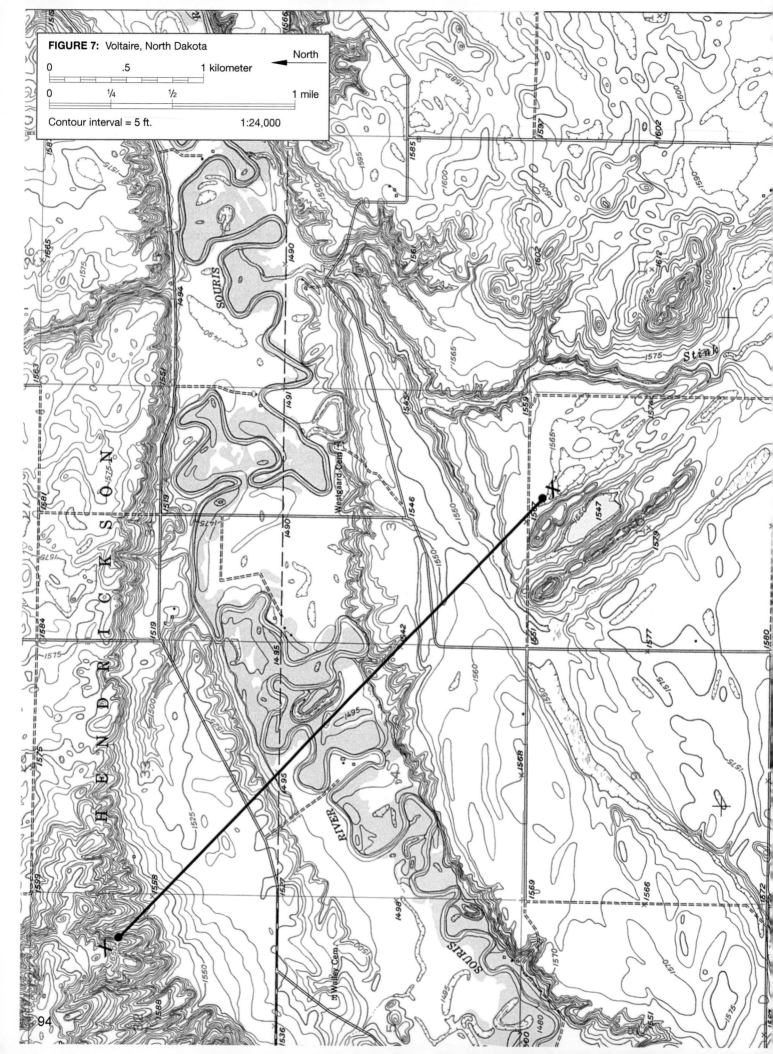

FIGURE 7: Voltaire, North Dakota

North

| 0 | | .5 | | 1 kilometer |

| 0 | | ¼ | | ½ | | 1 mile |

Contour interval = 5 ft.   1:24,000

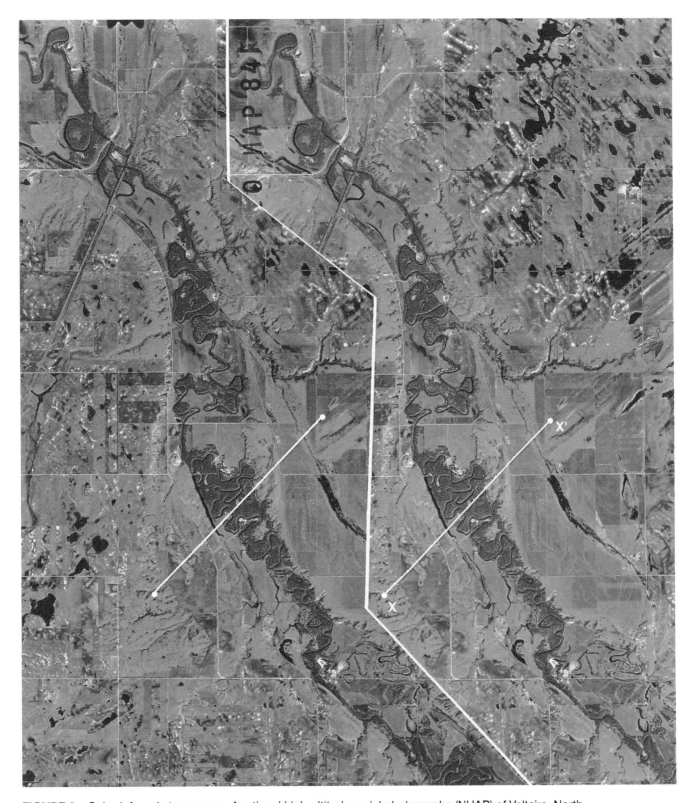

FIGURE 8 Color-infrared stereogram of national high-altitude aerial photographs (NHAP) of Voltaire, North Dakota, 1991. Scale 1:58,000. To view in stereo: (a) note that the figure is two images, (b) hold figure at arm's length, (c) cross your eyes until the two images become four images, (d) slightly relax your eyes so the two center images merge in stereo. (Courtesy of U.S. Geological Survey)

PART C: STREAM PROCESSES AND LANDSCAPES NEAR ENNIS, MONTANA

Some rivers are subject to large floods, either seasonal or periodic. In mountains, this flooding is due to snow melt. In deserts, it is caused by thunderstorms. During such times, rivers transport exceptionally large volumes of sediment. This causes characteristic features, two of which are braided channels and alluvial fans. Both features are relatively common in arid mountainous regions, such as the Ennis, Montana, area in Figures 9 and 10. (Both features also can occur wherever conditions are right, even at construction sites!)

Questions

15. What was the source of the sediments that have accumulated on the Cedar Creek Alluvial Fan?

16. What is the approximate stream gradient of:

    a. the main stream in the forested southeastern corner of the map (Figure 9) and stereogram (Figure 10)?

    b. most streams on the Cedar Creek Alluvial Fan?

    c. the Madison River?

17. What main stream channel types (shown in Figure 1B) are present on:

    a. the streams in the forested southeastern corner of the map (Figure 9) and stereogram (Figure 10)?

    b. the Cedar Creek Alluvial Fan?

    c. the valley of the Madison River (northwestern portion of Figure 9)?

18. How are the stream gradients and channel types described above (Questions 16 and 17) related?

19. How did the Cedar Creek Alluvial Fan form?

PART D: MEANDER EVOLUTION ON THE RIO GRANDE

Refer to Figure 11 showing the meandering Rio Grande, the river that forms the national border between Mexico and the United States. Notice that the position of the river changed in many places between 1936 (red line and leaders by lettered features) and 1992 (blue water bodies and leaders by lettered features). Study the meander terms provided in Figure 11, and then proceed to the questions below.

Questions

20. Study the meander cutbanks labeled **A** through **G.** The red leader from each letter points to the cutbank's location in 1936. The blue leader from each letter points to the cutbank's location in 1992. In what two general directions (relative to the meander, relative to the direction of river flow) have these cutbanks moved?

21. Study locations **H** and **I.**

    a. In what country were **H** and **I** located in 1936?

    b. In what country were **H** and **I** located in 1992?

    c. Explain a process that probably caused locations **H** and **I** to change from meanders to oxbow lakes.

22. Based on your answer in Question 21c, predict how the river will change in the future at locations **J** and **K.**

23. What are features **L, M,** and **N,** and what do they indicate about the historical path of the Rio Grande?

24. What is the average rate at which meanders like **A** through **G** migrated here (in meters per year) from 1936 to 1992? Explain your reasoning and calculations.

25. Explain in steps how a meander evolves from the earliest stage of its history as a broad slightly-sinuous meander to the stage when an oxbow lake forms.

26. Suggest as many factors as you can think of that could speed up changes in the location of the Rio Grande.

27. Suggest as many factors as you can think of that could slow down changes in the location of the Rio Grande.

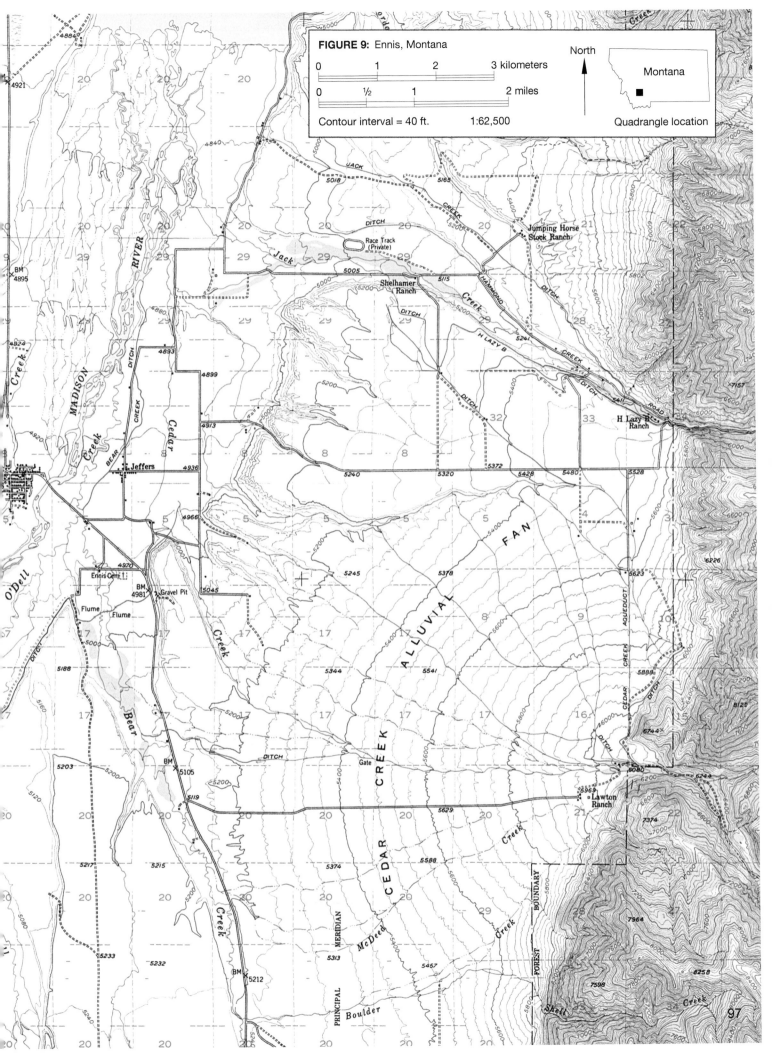

FIGURE 9: Ennis, Montana

North

Montana

Quadrangle location

Contour interval = 40 ft.   1:62,500

0   1   2   3 kilometers

0   ½   1   2 miles

97

FIGURE 10 Color-infrared stereogram of national high-altitude aerial photographs (NHAP) of Ennis, Montana, 1991. Scale 1:58,000. (Courtesy of U.S. Geological Survey)

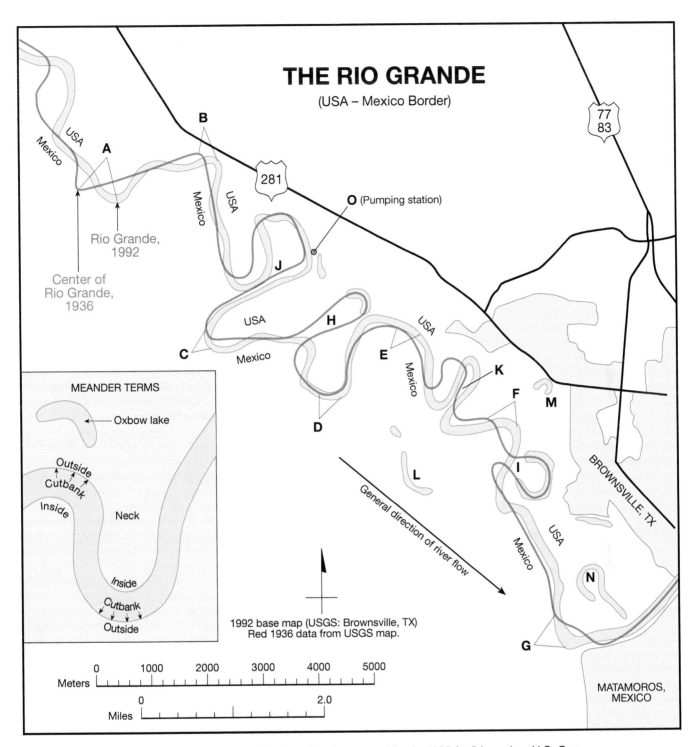

THE RIO GRANDE

(USA – Mexico Border)

Rio Grande, 1992

Center of Rio Grande, 1936

O (Pumping station)

MEANDER TERMS

Oxbow lake

Outside
Cutbank
Inside
Neck
Inside
Cutbank
Outside

General direction of river flow

1992 base map (USGS: Brownsville, TX)
Red 1936 data from USGS map.

| Meters | 0 | 1000 | 2000 | 3000 | 4000 | 5000 |

| Miles | 0 | | 2.0 |

BROWNSVILLE, TX

MATAMOROS, MEXICO

FIGURE 11 Map of the Rio Grande in 1992 (blue) and its former position in 1936 (red) based on U.S. Geological Survey topographic maps (Brownsville, Texas, 1992; West Brownsville, Texas, 1936). The river flows east-southeast. Note the inset box of meander terms used to describe features of meandering streams.

PART E: STREAM EROSION AND MASS WASTAGE AT NIAGARA FALLS

Mass wastage is the downslope movement of Earth materials such as soil, rock, and other debris. It is common along steep slopes, such as those created where rivers cut into the land. Some mass wastage occurs along the steep slopes of the river valleys. However, mass wastage can also occur in the bed of the river itself, as it does at Niagara Falls.

The Niagara River flows from Lake Erie to Lake Ontario (Figure 12). The gorge of the Niagara presents good evidence of the erosion of a caprock falls, Niagara Falls (Figure 13). The edge (caprock) of the falls is composed of the resistant Lockport Dolostone. The retreat of the falls is due to undercutting of mudstones that support the Lockport Dolostone. Water cascading from the lip of the falls enters the plunge pool with tremendous force, and the turbulent water easily erodes the soft mudstones. With the erosion of the mudstones, the Lockport Dolostone collapses.

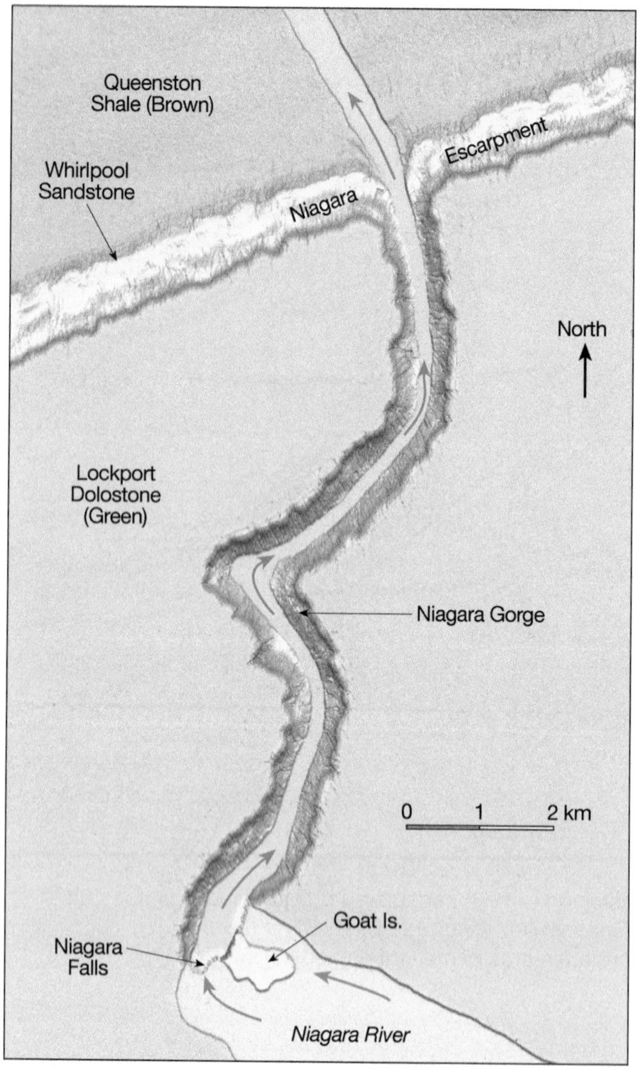

Questions

28. Geologic evidence indicates that the Niagara River began to cut its gorge (Niagara Gorge) about 11,000 years ago as the Laurentide Ice Sheet retreated from the area. The ice started at the Niagara Escarpment shown in Figure 12 and receded (melted back) north to form the basin of Lake Ontario. The Niagara Gorge started at the Niagara Escarpment and retreated south to its present location. Based on this geochronology and the length of Niagara Gorge, calculate the average rate of falls retreat in cm/year.

29. Name as many factors as you can that could cause the falls to retreat at a faster rate.

30. Name as many factors as you can that could cause the falls to retreat more slowly.

FIGURE 12 Map of the Niagara Gorge region of Canada and the United States. The Niagara River flows from Lake Erie north to Lake Ontario. Niagara Falls is located on the Niagara River at the head of Niagara Gorge, about half way between the two lakes.

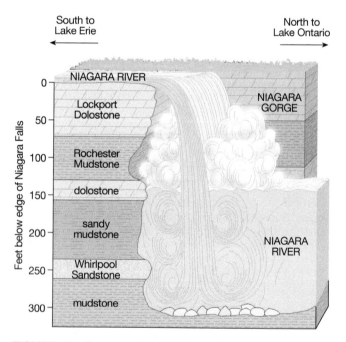

FIGURE 13 Cross section of Niagara Falls and geologic units of the Niagara escarpment.

31. Niagara Falls is about 35 km north of Lake Erie, and it is retreating southward. If the falls was to continue its retreat at the average rate calculated in Question 28, then how many years from now would the falls reach Lake Erie?

PART F: FLOOD HAZARD MAPPING, ASSESSMENT, AND RISKS

The water level and discharge of a river fluctuates from day to day, week to week, and month to month. These changes are measured at *gaging stations,* with a permanent water-level indicator and recorder. On a typical August day in downtown St. Louis, Missouri, the Mississippi River normally has a discharge of about 130,000 cubic feet of water per second and water levels well below the boat docks and concrete *levees* (retaining walls). However, at the peak of an historic 1993 flood, the river discharged more than a million cubic feet of water per second (8 times the normal amount), swept away docks, and reached water levels at the very edge of the highest levees.

When the water level of a river is below the river's banks, the river is at a **normal stage.** When the water level is even with the banks, the river is at **bankfull stage.** And when the water level exceeds (overflows) the banks, the river is at a **flood stage.** The Federal Emergency Management Agency (FEMA: **www.floodsmart.gov**) notes that there is a 26% chance that your home will be flooded over the 30-year period of a typical home mortgage (compared to a 9% chance of a home fire).

Early in July 1994, Tropical Storm Alberto entered Georgia and remained in a fixed position for several days. More than 20 inches of rain fell in west-central Georgia over those three days and caused severe flooding along the Flint River. Montezuma was one of the towns along the Flint River that was flooded.

This part of the laboratory is designed for you to map and assess the extent of flooding that occurred at Montezuma, based on river gage records and a $7\frac{1}{2}$-minute quadrangle map (Figure 14). You will then use river gage records to construct a flood magnitude/frequency graph, determine the probability of floods of specific magnitudes (flood levels), and revise a map of Montezuma to show the area that can be expected to be flooded by a 100-year flood.

Questions

32. On Figure 14, locate the gaging station along the east side of the Flint River near the center of the map, between Montezuma and Oglethorpe. This U.S. Geological Survey (USGS) gaging station is located at an elevation of 255.83 feet above sea level, and the river is considered to be at flood stage when it is 20 feet above this level (275.83 feet). The old flood record was 27.40 feet above the gaging station (1929), but the July 1994 flood established a new record at 35.11 feet above the gaging station, or 289.94 feet above sea level. This corresponds almost exactly to the 290 foot contour line on Figure 14. Trace the 290 foot contour line on both sides of the Flint River on Figure 14. Label the area within these contours (land areas lower than 290 feet) as the 1994 Flood Hazard Zone.

33. Assess the damage caused by the July 1994 flood.

a. Notice that the gaging station is located adjacent to highway 26-49-90. Was it possible to travel from Montezuma to Oglethorpe on this highway during the 1994 flood? Explain.

b. Notice the railroad tracks parallel to (and south of) highway 26-49-90 between Montezuma and Oglethorpe. Was it possible to travel on these railroads during the 1994 flood? Explain.

34. Notice line **X–Y** near the top center part of the map (Figure 14).

a. The map shows the Flint River at its normal stage. What is the width (in km) of the Flint River at its normal stage along line **X–Y**?

b. What was the width of the river (in km) along this line when it was at maximum flood stage (290 feet) during the July 1994 flood?

35. Notice the floodplain of the Flint River along line **X–Y**. It is the relatively flat (as indicated by widely-spaced contour lines) marshy land between the river and the steep (as indicated by more closely spaced contour lines) walls of the valley that are created by erosion during floods.

a. What is the elevation (in feet above sea level) of the floodplain on the west side of the river along line **X–Y**?

b. How deep (in feet above sea level) was the water that covered that floodplain during the 1994 flood? (Explain your reasoning or show your mathematical calculation.)

c. Did the 1994 flood (i.e., the highest river level ever recorded here) stay within the floodplain and its bounding valley slopes? Does this suggest that the 1994 flood was of normal or abnormal magnitude (severity) for this river? Explain your reasoning.

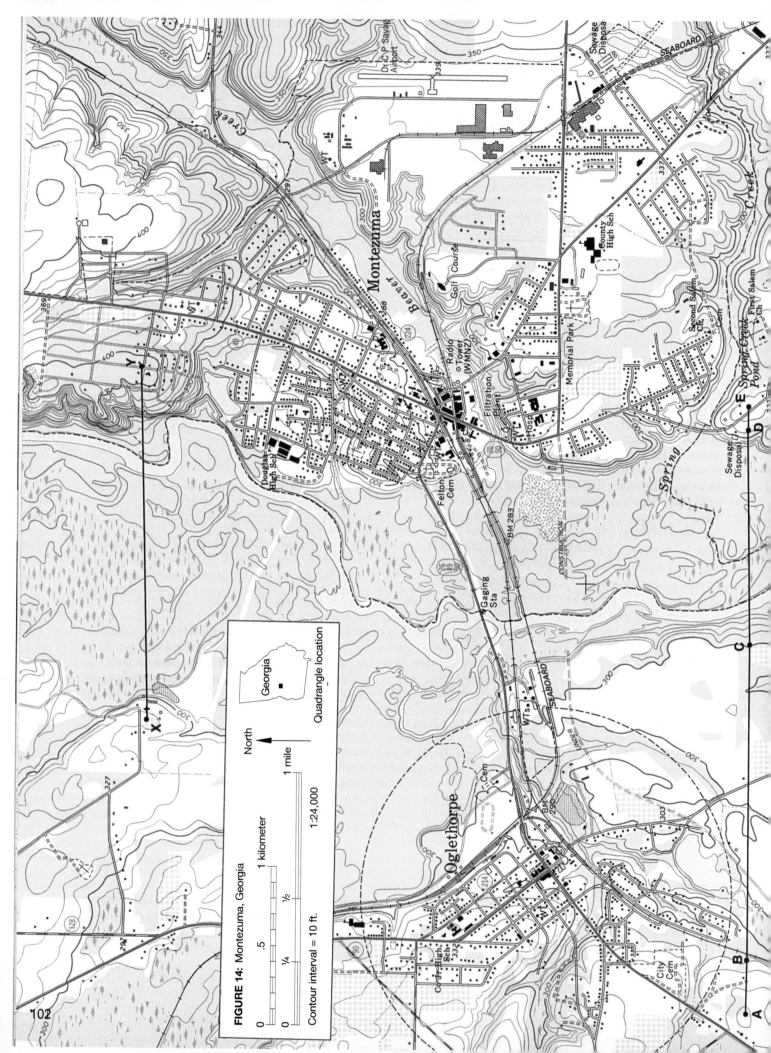

FIGURE 14: Montezuma, Georgia

0 ———————— .5 ———————— 1 kilometer

0 ——— 1/4 ——— 1/2 ——— 1 mile

1:24,000

Contour interval = 10 ft.

North

Georgia

Quadrangle location

36. The USGS recorded annual high stages (elevation of water level) of the Flint River at the Montezuma gaging station in Figure 14 for 99 years (1897 and 1905–2002). This raw data is available online at http://waterdata.usgs.gov/ga/nwis/inventory/?site_no=02349500. Parts of the data have been summarized in Figure 15.

a. The annual highest stages of the Flint River (S) were ranked in severity from S = 1 (highest annual high stage ever recorded; i.e., the 1994 flood) to S = 99 (lowest annual high stage). Data for 14 of these ranked years are provided in the table at the top of Figure 15 and can be used to calculate recurrence interval for each magnitude (rank, S). **Recurrence interval** (or **return period**) is the average number of years between occurrences of a flood of a given rank (S) or greater than that given rank. Recurrence interval for a rank of flood can be calculated as: RI = (n + 1)/S. Calculate the recurrence interval for ranks 1 – 5 and write them in the table at the top of Figure 15. This has already been done for ranks of 20, 30, 40, 50, 60, 70, 80, 90, and 99.

b. Notice (Figure 15) that a recurrence interval of 5.0 means that there is a 1-in-5 probability (or 20% chance) that an event of that magnitude will occur in any given year. This is known as a *5-year flood*. What is a *100-year flood*?

c. Plot (as exactly as you can) points on the flood magnitude/frequency graph (bottom of Figure 15) for all 14 ranks of annual high river stage in the table (top of Figure 15). Then use a ruler to draw a line through the points (and on to the right edge of the graph) so the number/distance of/to points above and below the line is similar.

d. Your completed flood magnitude/frequency graph can now be used to estimate the probability of future floods of a given magnitude and frequency. A 10-year flood on the Flint River is the point where the line in your graph crosses the flood frequency (RI, return period) of 10 years. What is the probability that a future 10-year flood will occur in any given year, and what will be its magnitude (river elevation in feet above sea level)?

e. What is the probability for any given year that a flood on the Flint River at Montezuma, GA will reach an elevation of 275 feet above sea level?

37. Most homeowners insurance policies do not insure against floods, even though floods cause more damage than any other natural hazard. Homeowners must obtain private or federal flood insurance in addition to their base homeowners policy. The National Flood Insurance Program (NFIP), a Division of the Federal Emergency Management Agency (FEMA) helps communities develop corrective and preventative measures for reducing future flood damage. The program centers on floodplain identification, mapping, and management. In return, members of these communities are eligible for discounts on federal flood insurance. The rates are determined on the basis of a community's FIRM (Flood Insurance Rate Map), an official map of the community on which FEMA has delineated flood *hazard areas* and *risk premium zones* (with discount rates). The hazard areas on a FIRM is defined on a *base flood elevation* (BFE)—the computed elevation to which flood water is estimated to rise during a *base flood*. The regulatory-standard base flood elevation is the 100-year flood elevation. Based on your graph (bottom of Figure 15), what is the BFE for Montezuma, GA?

38. The 1996 FEMA FIRM for Montezuma, GA shows hazard areas designated *zone A*. Zone A is the official designation for areas expected to be inundated by 100-year flooding even though no BFEs have been determined. The location of zone A (shaded gray) is shown on a portion of the Montezuma, GA $7\frac{1}{2}$ minute topographic quadrangle map in Figure 16. Your work above can be used to revise the flood hazard area. Place a dark line on this map (as carefully as you can) to show the elevation contour of the BFE for this community (your answer in item 37). Your revised map reflects more accurately what area will be inundated by a 100-year flood. In general, how is the BFE line that you have plotted different from the boundary of zone A plotted by FEMA on its 1996 FIRM?

39. Note that the elevation of the 100-year flood is estimated on the basis of historical (existing) data. As in the example of Montezuma, GA, a new flood that sets a new flood record will change the flood magnitude/frequency graph and the estimated BFE. You should always obtain the latest flood hazard map/graph to estimate flood probability for a given location. Determine the flood risk where you live (or another location of your choice) at **www.floodsmart.gov/floodsmart/pages/riskassesment/findpropertyform.jsp.**

40. If you live in an area that is prone to flooding, then what disaster supplies should you keep on hand (**www.fema.gov**)?

Rank of annual highest river stage (S)	Year (*n = 99)	River elevation above gage, in feet	Gage elevation above sea level, in feet	River elevation above sea level, in feet	Recurrence interval** (RI), in years	Probability of occurring in any given year	Percent chance of occurring in any given year***
1 (highest)	1994	34.11	255.83	289.9		1 in 100	1%
2	1929	27.40	255.83	283.2		1 in 50	2%
3	1990	26.05	255.83	281.9		1 in 33.3	3%
4	1897	26.00	255.83	281.8		1 in 25	4%
5	1949	25.20	255.83	281.0		1 in 20	5%
20	1928	21.30	255.83	277.1	5.0	1 in 5	20%
30	1912	20.60	255.83	276.4	3.4	1 in 3.4	29%
40	1959	19.30	255.83	275.1	2.3	1 in 2.3	43%
50	1960	18.50	255.83	274.3	2.0	1 in 2	50%
60	1934	17.70	255.83	273.5	1.8	1 in 1.8	56%
70	1974	17.25	255.83	273.1	1.5	1 in 1.5	67%
80	1967	14.76	255.83	270.6	1.3	1 in 1.3	77%
90	1907	13.00	255.83	268.8	1.1	1 in 1.1	91%
99 (lowest)	2002	8.99	255.83	264.7	1.0	1 in 1	100%

Recurrence Intervals for Selected, Ranked, Annual Highest Stages of the Flint River over 99 Years of Observation (1897 and 1905–2002) at Montezuma, Georgia (USGS Station 02349500, data from USGS)

*n = number of years of annual observations = 99
**Recurrence Interval (RI) = (n + 1) / S = average number of years between occurrences of an event of this magnitude or greater.
***Percent chance of occurrence = 1 / RI x 100.

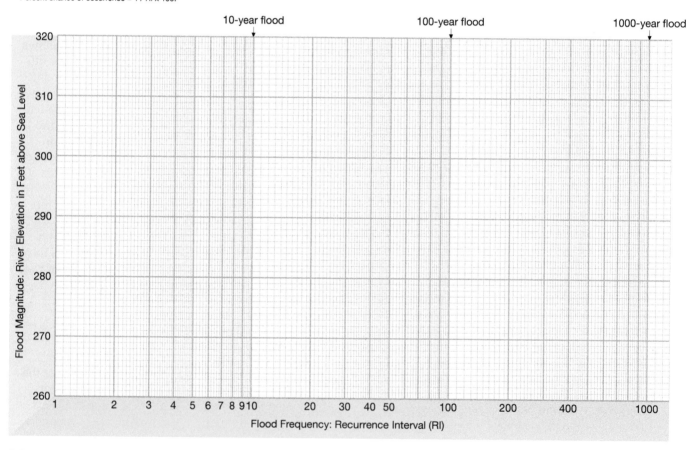

FIGURE 15   Flint River, GA historical data (USGS) and flood magnitude/frequency graph.

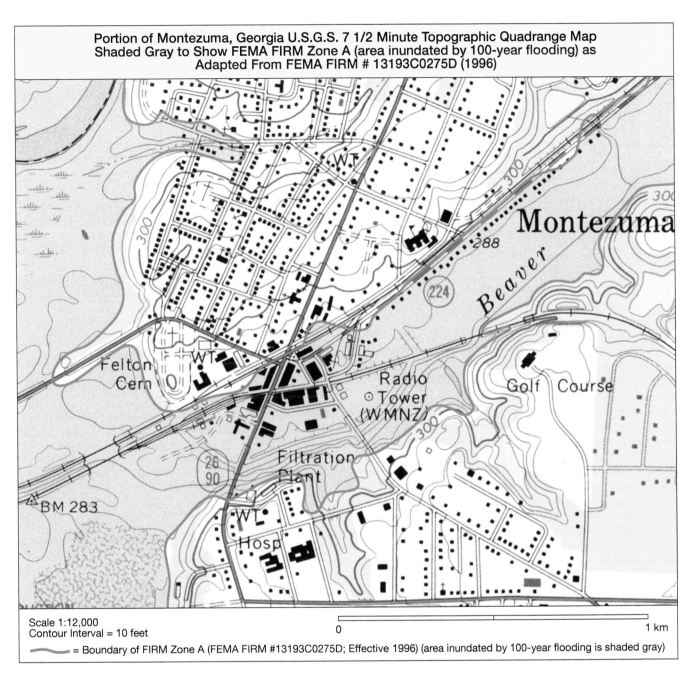

FIGURE 16 Flood hazard map of Montezuma, GA.

Groundwater Processes, Resources, and Risks

•CONTRIBUTING AUTHORS•

Gary D. McKenzie • *Ohio State University*

Richard N. Strom • *University of South Florida, Tampa*

James R. Wilson • *Weber State College*

OBJECTIVES

A. Understand the topographic features and groundwater movements associated with *karst topography.*

B. Construct a water-table contour map and determine the rate and direction of groundwater movement.

C. Evaluate how groundwater withdrawal can cause *subsidence* (sinking) of the land.

D. Evaluate hazards and risks associated with the use and contamination of groundwater.

MATERIALS

Pencil, eraser, ruler, and calculator.

INTRODUCTION

Water that seeps into the ground is pulled downward by the force of gravity through spaces in the soil and *bedrock* (rock that is exposed at the land surface or underlies the soil). At first, the water fills just some spaces and air remains in the other spaces. This underground zone with water- and air-filled spaces is called the *zone of aeration* (Figure 1; also called the *undersaturated zone* or *vadose zone*). Eventually, the water reaches a zone below the zone of aeration, where all spaces are completely saturated with water. This water-logged zone is called the *zone of saturation,* and its upper surface is the **water table** (Figure 1). Water in the saturated zone is called **groundwater,** which can also be withdrawn from the ground through a **well** (a hole dug or drilled into the ground). Most wells are lined with *casing,* a heavy metal or plastic pipe. The casing is perforated in sections where water is expected to supply the well. Other sections of the casing are left impervious to prevent unwanted rock particles or fluids from entering the well.

Recall the last time that you consumed a drink from a fast-food restaurant (a paper cup containing ice and liquid that you drink using a plastic straw). The mixture of ice and liquid (no air) at the bottom of the cup was a zone of saturation, and your straw was a well. Each time you sucked on the straw, you withdrew liquid from the drink container just as a homeowner withdraws water from a water well. After you drank some of the drink, the cup contained both a zone of saturation (water and ice in the bottom of the cup) and a zone of aeration (ice and mostly air in the upper part of the cup). The boundary between these two zones was a water table. In order to continue drinking the liquid, you had to be sure that the bottom of your straw was within the zone of saturation, below the water table. Otherwise, sucking on the straw produced only a slurping sound, and you obtained mostly air. Natural water wells work the same way. The wells must be drilled or dug to a point below the water table (within the zone of saturation), so water can flow or be pumped out of the ground.

From *Laboratory Manual in Physical Geology*, Eighth Edition, American Geological Institute, National Association of Geoscience Teachers, Richard M. Busch, Dennis Tasa. Copyright © 2009 by American Geological Institute. Published by Pearson Prentice Hall. All rights reserved.

Water Table Contours and Flow Lines

A. Groundwater Zones and the Water Table

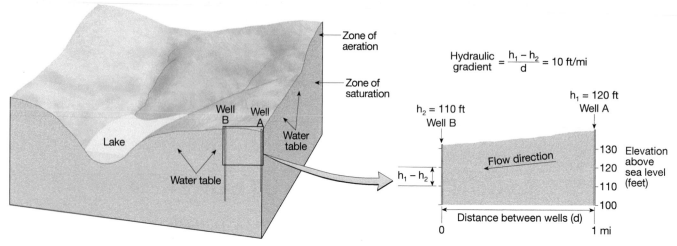

$$\text{Hydraulic gradient} = \frac{h_1 - h_2}{d} = 10 \text{ ft/mi}$$

B. Normal Water Table Contours and Flow Lines:
Note that flow direction is downhill to streams and the lake

C. Water Table Contours and Flow Lines Changed by a
Cone of Depression Developed Around a Pumped Well

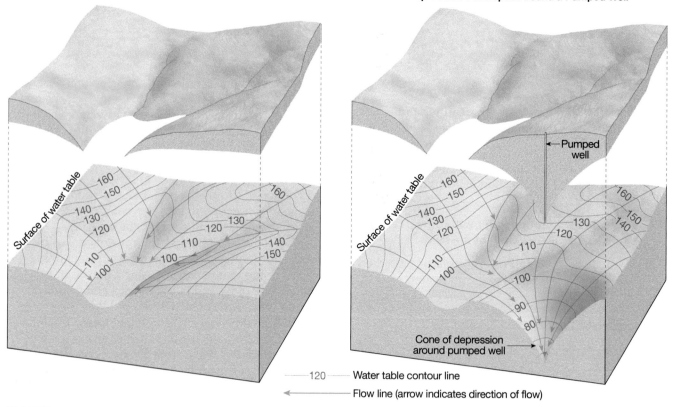

—— 120 —— Water table contour line

←————— Flow line (arrow indicates direction of flow)

FIGURE 1 Water movement through an unconfined aquifer. **A.** Rainwater seeps into the *zone of aeration* (undersaturated zone, vadose zone), where void spaces are filled with air and water. Below it is the *zone of saturation,* where all void spaces are filled with water. Its upper surface is the **water table.** Water in the saturated zone is called **groundwater,** which always flows down the hydraulic gradient in unconfined aquifers. **B.** A water table surface is rarely level. Contour lines (contours) are used to map its topography and identify flow lines—paths traveled by droplets of water from the points where they enter the water table to the points where they enter a lake or stream. **Flow lines** run perpendicular to contour lines, converge or diverge, but never cross. **C.** A pumped well is being used to withdraw water faster than it can be replenished, causing development of a **cone of depression** in the water table and a change in the groundwater flow lines.

The volume of void space (space filled with water or air) in sediment or bedrock is termed *porosity.* The larger the voids, and the greater their number, the higher is the porosity. If void spaces are interconnected, then fluids (water and air) can migrate through them (from space to space), and the rock or sediment is said to be *permeable.* Sponges and paper towels are household items that are permeable, because liquids easily flow into and through them. Plastic and glass are *impermeable* materials, so they are used to contain fluids.

Permeable bedrock materials make good **aquifers,** or rock strata that conduct water. Some examples are sandstones and limestones. Impermeable bedrock materials prevent the flow of water and are called **confining beds.** Some examples are layers of clay, mudstone, shale, or dense igneous and metamorphic rock. But how does groundwater move through aquifers?

When aquifers are sandwiched between confining beds, the groundwater fills them from confining bed to confining bed—like water filling a large, flat pipe. When aquifers are not confined, the groundwater establishes a water table just beneath the surface of the land (Figure 1). For this reason, unconfined aquifers are sometimes called *water table aquifers.*

Groundwater in an unconfined aquifer is pulled down by gravity and attempts to spread out through the ground until it forms the water table surface (such as the one in the drink cup described above). You can see the water table where it leaves the ground and becomes the level surface of a lake (Figure 1A). However, because groundwater is continuously being replenished (recharged) upslope, and it takes time for the water to flow through the ground, the water table is normally not level. It is normally higher uphill, where water flows into the ground, and lower downhill, where water seeps out of the ground at lakes, streams, or springs. The slope of the water table surface is called the **hydraulic gradient** (Figure 1A)—the difference in elevation between two points on the water table (observed in wells or surfaces of lakes and ponds) divided by the distance between those points.

To better understand the topography of the water table in a region, geologists measure its elevation wherever they can find it in wells or where it forms the surfaces of lakes and streams. The elevation data is then contoured to map the **water table contour lines** (Figure 1). Since water always flows down the shortest and steepest path (path of highest hydraulic gradient) it can find, a drop of water on the water table surface will flow perpendicular to the slope of the water table contour lines. Geologists use **flow lines** with arrows to show the paths that water droplets will travel from the point where they enter

the water table to the point where they reach a lake, stream, or level water table surface. Notice how flow lines have been plotted on Figure 1B and 1C. In Figure 1C, notice how a pumped well is being used to withdraw water faster than it can be replenished. This has caused a cone-shaped depression in the water table (**cone of depression**) and a change in the regional flow of the groundwater. Thus, water table contour maps are useful for determining:

- paths of water flow (flow lines on a map) along which hydraulic gradients are normally measured

- where the water comes from for a particular well

- paths (flow lines) that contaminants in groundwater will likely follow from their source.

- changes to groundwater flow lines and hydraulic gradients caused by cones of depression at pumped wells.

PART A: CAVES AND KARST TOPOGRAPHY

The term **karst** describes a distinctive topography that indicates dissolution of underlying soluble rock, generally limestone (Figure 2). The limestone dissolves because rainwater is mildly acidic. The rainwater soaks into the ground to form acidic groundwater, which dissolves the calcite mineral crystals making up the limestone.

Rainwater may contain several acids, but the most common is carbonic acid (H_2CO_3). It forms when water (H_2O) and carbon dioxide (CO_2) combine in the atmosphere. When it rains, the carbonic acid in rainwater dissolves the calcite (and other carbonate minerals) in limestone by this reaction:

$$CaCO_3 \quad + \quad H_2CO_3 \quad = \quad Ca^{+2} \quad + \quad 2\,HCO_3^{-1}$$

| calcite | carbonic acid | calcium ions dissolved in groundwater | bicarbonate ions dissolved in groundwater |

A typical karst topography has these features, which are illustrated in Figure 2 and visible on the topographic map in Figure 3.

- **Sinkholes**—surface depressions formed by the collapse of caves or other large underground void spaces.

- **Solution valleys**—valley-like depressions formed by a linear series of sinkholes or collapse of the roof of a linear cave.

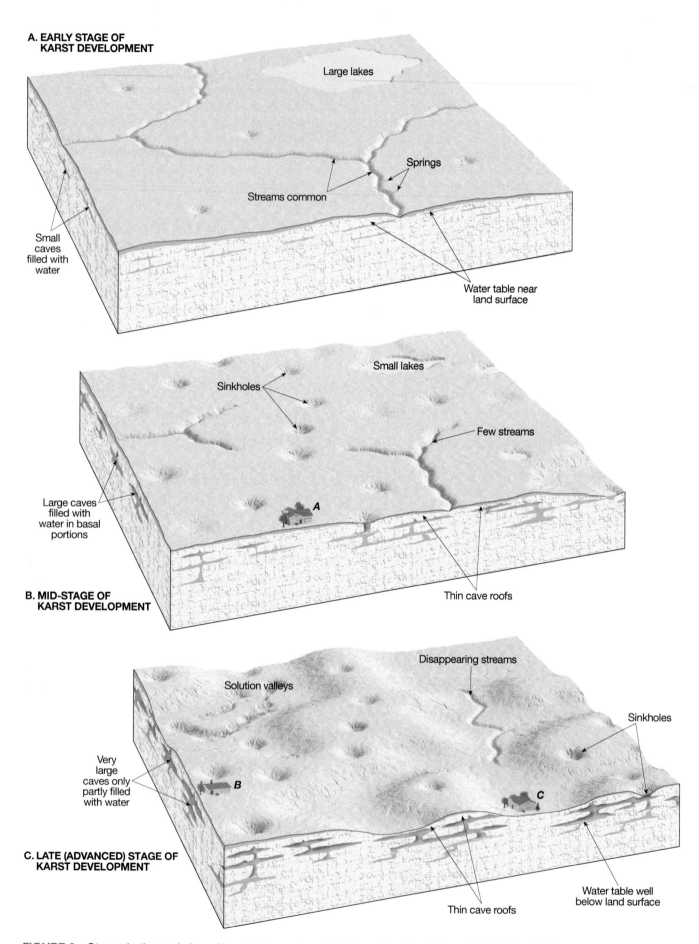

A. EARLY STAGE OF KARST DEVELOPMENT

Large lakes

Springs

Streams common

Small caves filled with water

Water table near land surface

Sinkholes

Small lakes

Few streams

Large caves filled with water in basal portions

A

Thin cave roofs

B. MID-STAGE OF KARST DEVELOPMENT

Disappearing streams

Solution valleys

Sinkholes

Very large caves only partly filled with water

B

C

C. LATE (ADVANCED) STAGE OF KARST DEVELOPMENT

Thin cave roofs

Water table well below land surface

FIGURE 2 Stages in the evolution of karst topography, which forms by dissolution of soluble bedrock.

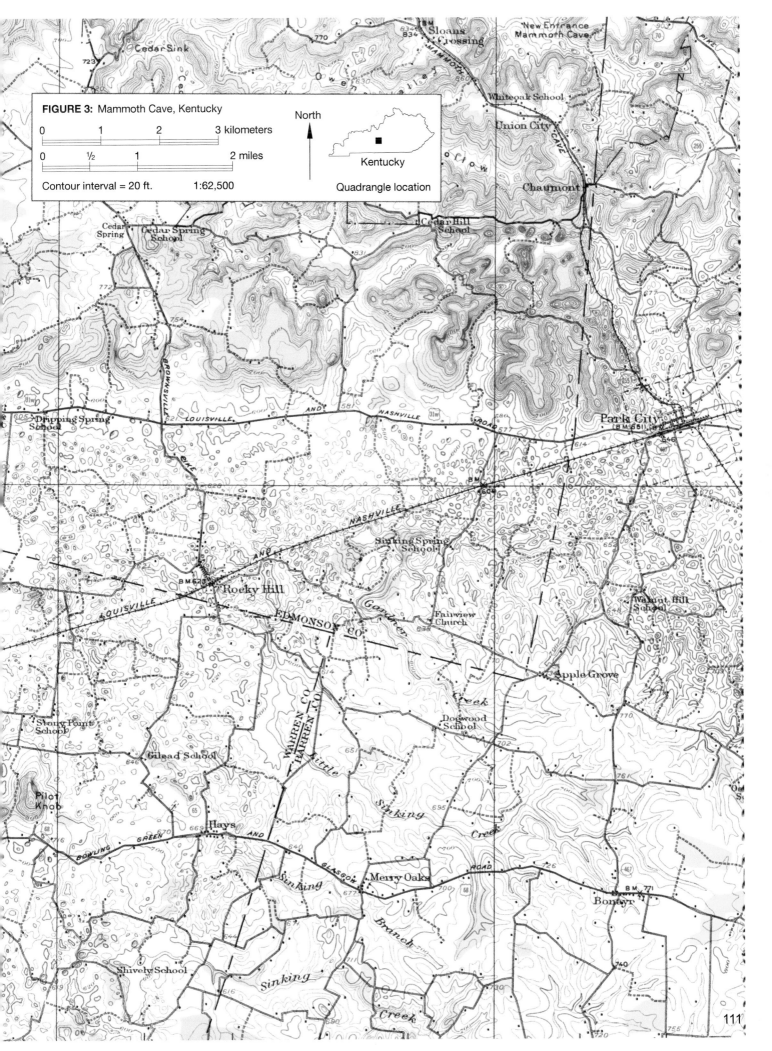

FIGURE 3: Mammoth Cave, Kentucky

0   1   2   3 kilometers

0   ½   1   2 miles

Contour interval = 20 ft.   1:62,500

North

Kentucky

Quadrangle location

111

- **Springs**—places where water flows naturally from the ground (from spaces in the bedrock).

- **Disappearing streams**—streams that terminate abruptly by seeping into the ground.

Much of the drainage in karst areas occurs underground rather than by surface runoff. Rainwater seeps into the ground along fractures in the bedrock (Figure 4), whereupon the acidic water dissolves the limestone around it. The cracks widen into narrow **caves** (underground cavities large enough for a person to enter), which may eventually widen into huge cave galleries. Sinkholes develop where the ceilings of these galleries collapse, and lakes or ponds form wherever water fills the sinkholes. The systems of fractures and caves that typically develop in limestones are what make limestones good aquifers.

Eventually, the acidic water that was *dissolving* limestone becomes so enriched in calcium and bicarbonate that it turns alkaline (the opposite of acid) and may actually begin *precipitating* calcite.

Caves in karst areas often have *stalactites*, icicle-like masses of chemical limestone that hang from cave ceilings (Figure 5). They form because calcite precipitates from water droplets as they drip from the cave ceiling. Water dripping onto the cave floor also can precipitate calcite and form more stout *stalagmites*.

Questions

1. Study Figure 4. Notice that there is no soil developed on this limestone bedrock surface, yet abundant plants are growing along linear features in the bedrock. What does this indicate about how water travels through bedrock in this part of Oklahoma?

2. If you had to drill a water well in the area pictured in Figure 4, then where would you drill (relative to the linear pattern of plant growth) to find a good supply of water? Explain your reasoning.

3. How is Figure 5 related to Figure 4?

4. It is common for buildings to sink into newly formed sinkholes as they develop in karst regions. Consider the three new-home construction sites (labeled **A, B,** and **C**) in Figure 2, relative to sinkhole hazards.

   a. Which new-home construction site (**A, B,** or **C**) is the **most** hazardous? Why?

   b. Which new-home construction site (**A, B,** or **C**) is the **least** hazardous? Why?

   c. Imagine that you are planning to buy a new-home construction site in the region portrayed in Figure 2. What could you do to find out if there is a sinkhole hazard in the location where you are thinking of building your home?

5. Study the portion of the Mammoth Cave (Kentucky) topographic map in Figure 3. This area is underlain by limestone, which is capped (overlain) by sandstone in the northern part of the mapped area (north of Park City).

   a. How can you tell the area on this map where limestone crops out at Earth's surface?

   b. Draw and label a line on Figure 3 that separates the karst topography from the northern part of the map where mostly forested (green color) sandstone crops out.

   c. Find and label a disappearing stream at the end where it disappears within the karst region.

   d. Find and label a lake that formed by flooding a sinkhole.

   e. Find and label a solution valley anywhere on the map.

   f. Imagine that you are planning to build a home on top of one of the highest hills in the area where mostly sandstone crops out, and that you plan to use well water drawn from the limestone under your property. What is the deepest you would have to drill your well (through the sandstone) to obtain water from the limestone aquifer? Explain your reasoning.

   g. Why are there so few sinkholes developed in the southeast part of this map area (even though limestone crops out there)?

FIGURE 4   Looking east toward the Arkansas River from Vap's Pass, Oklahoma (15 miles northeast of Ponca City). The Fort Riley Limestone bedrock *crops out* (is exposed at the surface) here. There is no soil in this location, but plants have grown naturally along linear features in the bedrock.

FIGURE 5   Stalactites on part of the ceiling of Cave of the Winds, which has formed in Paleozoic lime-stones near Manitou Springs, Colorado.

PART B: LOCATION AND MOVEMENT OF GROUNDWATER IN THE FLORIDAN LIMESTONE AQUIFER

Figures 6–8 show karst features developed in the Floridan Limestone Aquifer in the northern part of Tampa, Florida. Notice in Figures 6 and 7 that most of the lakes occupy sinkholes. They are indicated on Figure 6 with hachured contour lines (contours with small tick marks that point inward, indicating a depression). These depressions intersect the water table and the subjacent limestone bedrock, as shown in Figure 7. By determining and mapping the elevations of water surfaces in the lakes, you can determine the slope of the water table and the direction of flow of the groundwater here (as in Figure 1B).

Questions

6. On Figure 8, mark the elevations of water levels in the lakes (obtain this information from Figure 6). The elevations of Lake Magdalene and some lakes beyond the boundaries of the topographic map already are marked for you.

7. Contour the water-table surface (use a 5-foot contour interval) on Figure 8. Draw only contour lines representing whole fives (40, 45, and so on).

8. The flow of shallow groundwater in Figure 8 is at right angles to the contour lines. The groundwater flows from high elevations to lower elevations, just like a stream. Draw three or four flow lines with arrows on Figure 8 to indicate the direction of shallow groundwater flow in this part of Tampa. The southeastern part of Figure 6 shows numerous closed depressions but very few lakes. What does this indicate about the level of the water table in this region?

9. Note the Poinsettia Sinks, a pair of sinkholes in the southeast corner of the topographic map (see Figure 6). Note their closely spaced hachured contour lines. Next find the cluster of five similar sinkholes, called Blue Sinks, about 1 mile northwest of Poinsettia Sinks (just west of the WHBO radio tower). Use asterisks (*) to mark their locations on Figure 8, and label them "Blue Sinks."

a. Draw a straight arrow (vector) on Figure 8 along the shortest path between Blue Sinks and Poinsettia Sinks. The water level in Blue Sinks is

15 feet above sea level, and the water level in Poinsettia Sinks is 10 feet above sea level. Calculate the hydraulic gradient (in ft/mi) along this arrow and write it next to the arrow on Figure 8. (Refer to Figure 1 to review hydraulic gradient as needed.)

b. On Figure 6, note the stream and valley north of Blue Sinks. This is a fairly typical disappearing stream. Draw its approximate course onto Figure 8. Make an arrowhead on one end of your drawing of the stream to indicate the direction that water flows in this stream. How does this direction compare to the general slope of the water table?

10. In March 1958, fluorescent dye was injected into the northernmost of the Blue Sinks. It was detected 28 hours later in Sulphur Springs, on the Hillsborough River to the south (see Figure 8). Use this data to calculate the approximate velocity of flow in this portion of the Floridan Aquifer:

a. in feet per hour

b. in miles per hour

c. in meters per hour

The velocities you just calculated are quite high, even for the Floridan Aquifer. But this portion of Tampa seems to be riddled with solution channels and caves in the underlying limestone. Sulphur Springs has an average discharge of approximately 44 cubic feet per second (cfs), and its maximum recorded discharge was 165 cfs (it once was a famous spa).

11. During recent years, the discharge at Sulphur Springs has decreased. Water quality has also worsened substantially.

a. Examine the human-made structures on Figure 6. Note especially those in red, the color used to indicate new structures. Why do you think the discharge of Sulphur Springs has decreased in recent years?

b. Why do you think the water quality has decreased in recent years?

12. Imagine you are selling homeowner's insurance in the portion of the Sulphur Springs quadrangle shown in Figure 6. List all the potential groundwater-related hazards to homes and homeowners in the area that you can think of.

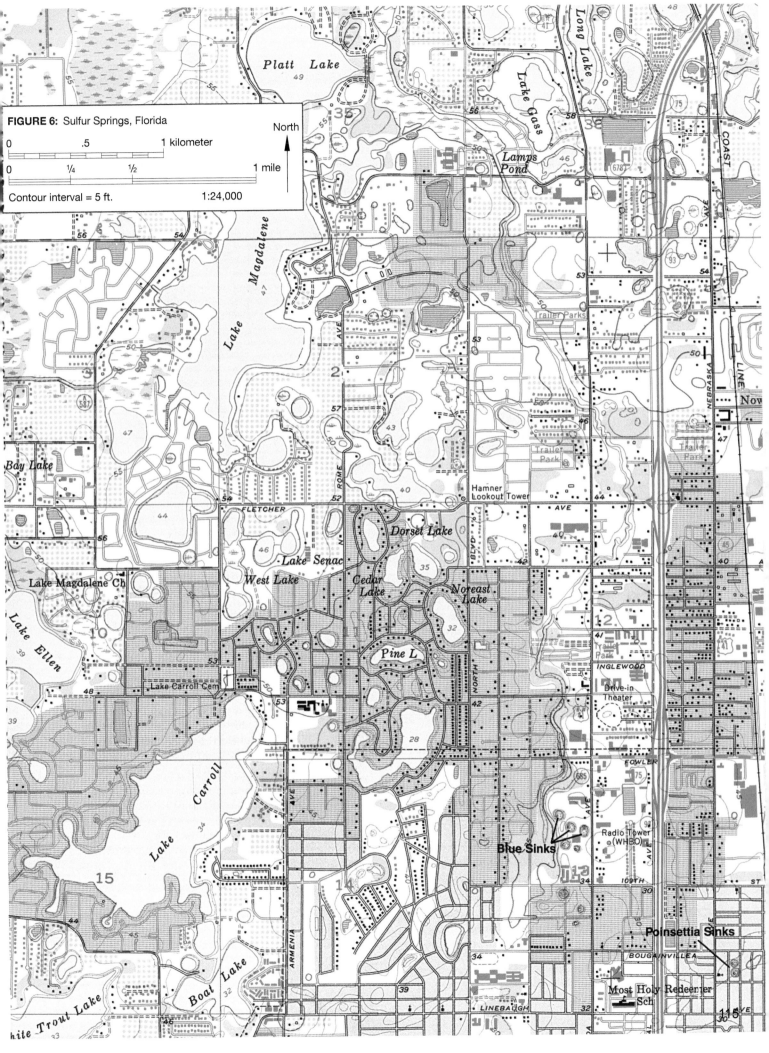

FIGURE 6: Sulfur Springs, Florida

North

0 .5 1 kilometer

0 1/4 1/2 1 mile

Contour interval = 5 ft. 1:24,000

Platt Lake

Long Lake

Lake Gass

Lamps Pond

Lake Magdalene

Bay Lake

Trailer Parks

Trailer Park

Hamner Lookout Tower

FLETCHER

Dorset Lake

Lake Magdalene Ch

Lake Senac

West Lake

Cedar Lake

Noreast Lake

Pine L

Lake Ellen

Lake Carroll Cem

Trailer Park

INGLEWOOD

Drive-in Theater

FOWLER

Lake Carroll

Blue Sinks

Radio Tower (WHBO)

Poinsettia Sinks

BOUGAINVILLEA

Most Holy Redeemer Sch

LINEBAUGH

White Trout Lake

Boat Lake

NEBRASKA

COAST LINE

ROME

ARMENIA

109TH ST

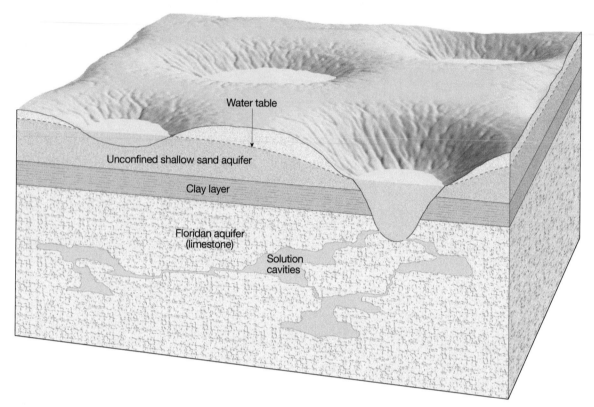

FIGURE 7 Geologic cross section showing groundwater distribution in strata underlying the Tampa, Florida, area.

PART C: LAND SUBSIDENCE HAZARDS CAUSED BY GROUNDWATER WITHDRAWAL

Land subsidence caused by human withdrawal of groundwater is a serious problem in many places throughout the world. For example, in the heart of Mexico City, the land surface has gradually subsided up to 7.6 m (25 ft). At the northern end of California's Santa Clara Valley, 17 square mi of land have subsided below the highest tide level in San Francisco Bay and now must be protected by earthworks. Other centers of subsidence include Houston, Tokyo, Venice, and Las Vegas. With increasing withdrawal of groundwater and more intensive use of the land surface, we can expect the problem of subsidence to become more widespread.

Subsidence induced by withdrawal of groundwater commonly occurs in areas underlain by stream-deposited (alluvial) sand and gravel that is interbedded with lake-deposited (lacustrine) clays and clayey silts (Figure 9A). The sand-and-gravel beds are aquifers, and the clay and clayey silt beds are confining beds.

In Figure 10, the water in the lower aquifer ("sand and gravel") is confined between impermeable beds of clay and silt and is under pressure from its own weight. Thus, water in wells **A** and **C** rises to the *potentiometric (water-pressure) surface*. Such wells are termed **artesian wells** (water flows naturally from the top of the well) The sand in the water table aquifer (Figure 10) contains water that is not confined under pressure, so it is an *unconfined aquifer*. The water in well **B** stands at the level of the water table and must be pumped up to the land surface.

Land subsidence (Figure 9B) is related to the compressibility of water-saturated sediments. Withdrawing water from wells not only removes water from the system, it also lowers the potentiometric surface and reduces the water pressure in the confined artesian aquifers. As the water pressure is reduced, the aquifer is gradually compacted and the ground surface above it is gradually lowered. The hydrostatic pressure can be restored by replenishing (or **recharging**) the aquifer with water. But the confining beds, once compacted, will not expand to their earlier thicknesses.

The Santa Clara Valley (Figure 11) was one of the first areas in the United States where land subsidence due to groundwater overdraft was recognized. The Santa Clara Valley is a large structural trough filled

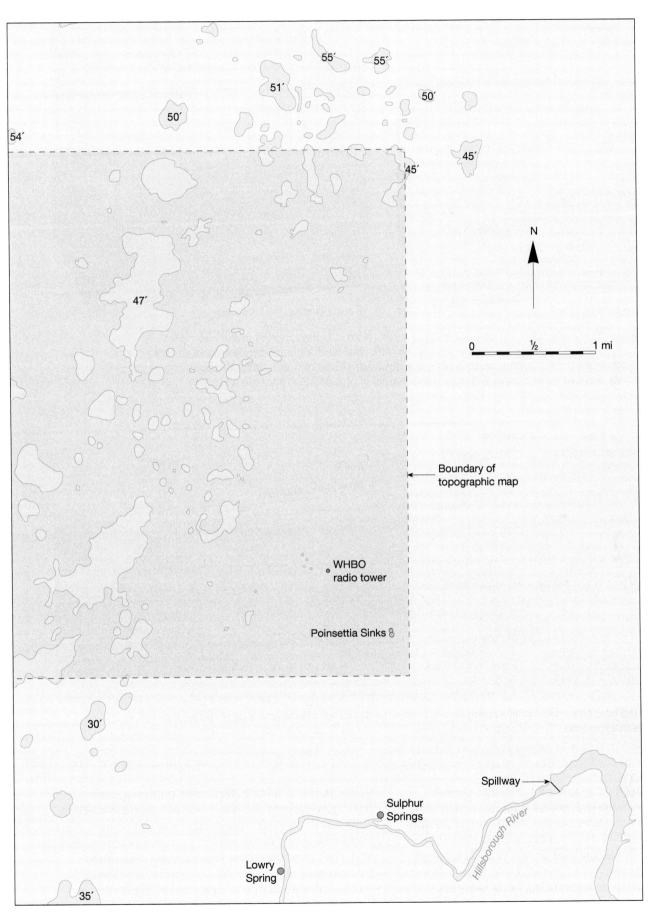

FIGURE 8 Sketch map of the area shown in Figure 6 (topographic map) and neighboring areas to the north, east, and south.

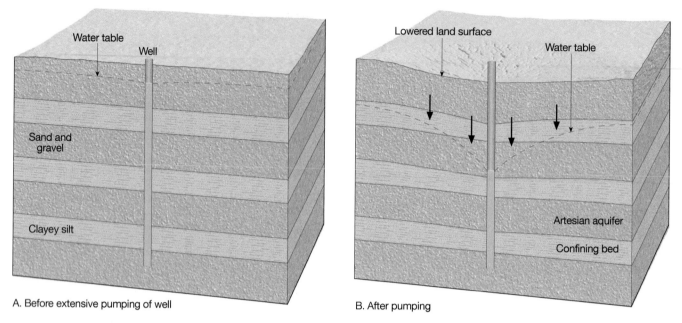

Water table
Well
Sand and gravel
Clayey silt

A. Before extensive pumping of well

Lowered land surface
Water table
Artesian aquifer
Confining bed

B. After pumping

FIGURE 9 Before (**A**) and after (**B**) extensive pumping of a well. Note in **B** the lowering of the water-pressure surface, compaction of confining beds between the aquifers, and resulting subsidence of land surface. Arrows indicate the direction of compaction caused by the downward force of gravity, after the opposing water pressure was reduced by excessive withdrawal (discharge) of groundwater from the well.

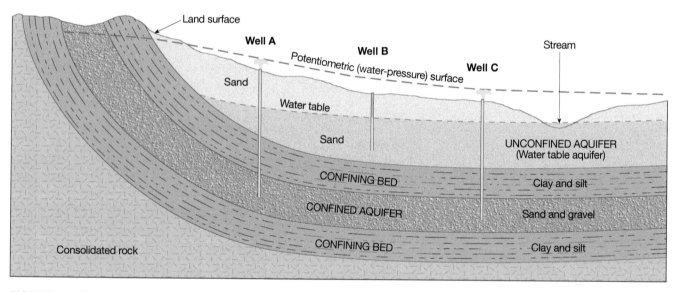

Land surface
Well A
Well B
Potentiometric (water-pressure) surface
Well C
Stream
Sand
Water table
Sand
UNCONFINED AQUIFER (Water table aquifer)
CONFINING BED
Clay and silt
CONFINED AQUIFER
Sand and gravel
CONFINING BED
Clay and silt
Consolidated rock

FIGURE 10 Geologic cross section illustrating an unconfined (water-table) aquifer and a confined aquifer. Vertical scale is exaggerated.

with alluvium (river sediments) more than 460 m (1500 ft) thick. Sand-and-gravel aquifers predominate near the valley margins, but the major part of the alluvium is silt and clay. Below a depth of 60 m (200 ft), the groundwater is confined by layers of clay, except near the margins.

Initially, wells as far south as Santa Clara were artesian, because the water-pressure surface was

above the land surface. However, pumping them for irrigation lowered the water-pressure surface 40–60 m (150–200 ft) by 1965. This decline was not continuous; natural recharge of the aquifer occurred between 1938 and 1947, in part because of controlled infiltration from surface reservoirs. As of 1971, the subsidence had been stopped due to a reversal of the water-level decline.

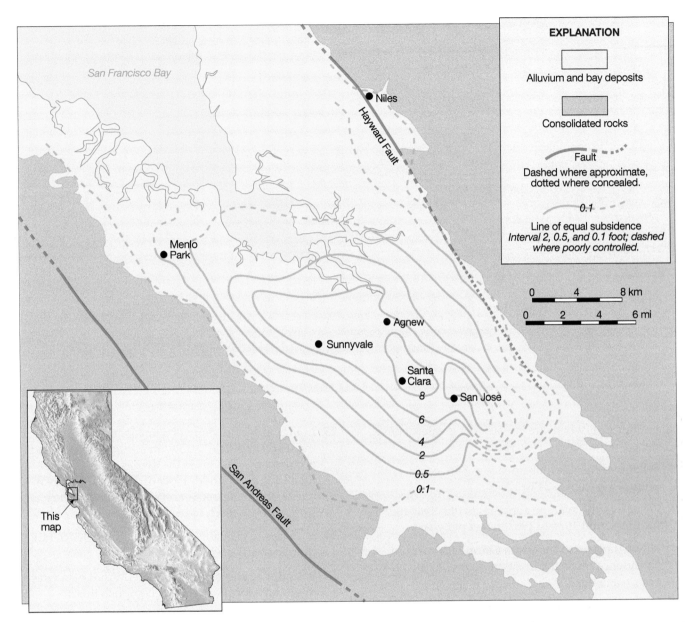

FIGURE 11 Land subsidence, 1934–1967, in the Santa Clara Valley, California. (Courtesy of U.S. Geological Survey)

Most wells tapping the artesian system are 150–300 m (500–1000 ft) deep, although a few reach 365 m (1200 ft). Well yields in the valley are 500–1500 gallons per minute (gpm), which is very high.

Questions

13. On Figure 12, solid brown contour lines show land surface elevation. Dashed blue lines represent the water-pressure surface (potentiometric surface) of a confined aquifer, as shown

in Figure 10. This is the height to which water will rise in a well that is drilled into the aquifer.

a. Find and connect the points on Figure 12 where the two sets of contour lines have the same elevation.

b. Shade in the area on this same figure where wells would flow at the land surface without having to be pumped (i.e., where wells would be artesian).

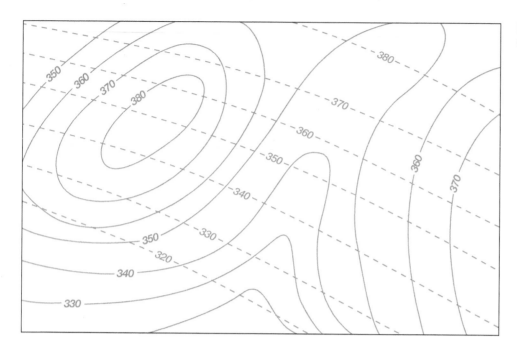

FIGURE 12 Graph of water data for Question 13.

14. In Figure 11, where are the areas of greatest subsidence in the Santa Clara Valley?

15. What was the total subsidence at San Jose (Figure 13) from 1934 to 1967?

16. What was the average annual rate of subsidence for the period 1934 to 1967 in feet per year?

17. At what places in the Santa Clara Valley would subsidence cause the most problems? Explain your reasoning.

18. Would you expect much subsidence to occur in the darker shaded areas of Figure 11? Explain.

19. By 1960, the total subsidence at San Jose had reached 9.0 feet (Figure 13). What was the average annual rate of subsidence (in feet per year) for the seven-year period from 1960 through 1967?

20. Refer to Figure 14. What was the level of the water in the San Jose well in:

   a. 1915?

   b. 1967?

21. During what period would the San Jose well have been a flowing artesian well? Explain.

22. How can you explain the minor fluctuations in the hydrograph (Figure 14) like those between 1920 and 1925?

23. In Figure 14, the slope of a line joining the level of the land surface in 1915 with subsidence that had occurred by 1967 gives the average rate of subsidence for that period. How did the rate of subsidence occurring between 1935 and 1948 differ from earlier rates?

24. Explain the probable cause of the subsidence rate change noted in Question 23.

25. Subsidence was stopped by 1971. What measures might have been taken to accomplish this?

Year	Total Subsidence (feet) from 1912 level
1912	0.0
1920	0.3
1934	4.6
1935	5.0
1936	5.0
1937	5.2
1940	5.5
1948	5.8
1955	8.0
1960	9.0
1963	11.0
1967	12.7

FIGURE 13 Subsidence at benchmark P7 in San Jose, California.

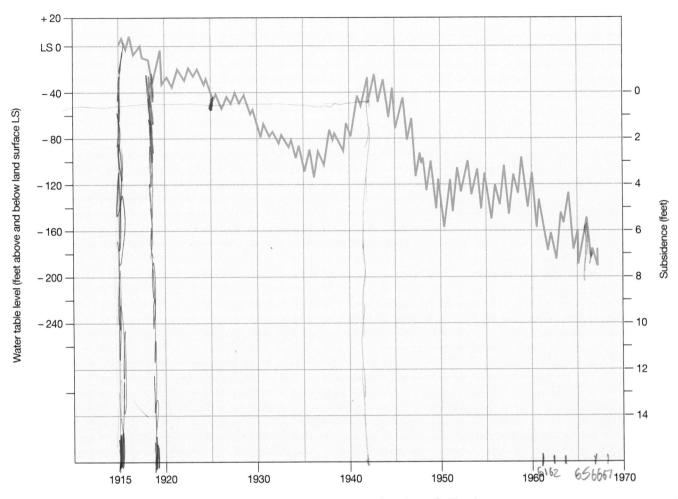

FIGURE 14 Hydrograph showing changes of water level in a well at San Jose, California.

PART D: HOME SEPTIC SYSTEMS AND GROUNDWATER CONTAMINATION

Many homes are not connected to a public sewage treatment system. Owners of these homes must have on-site sewage disposal systems that are properly located, constructed, and maintained. Otherwise, septic-system failure, groundwater contamination, and health hazards may develop. Such hazards place people's health and lives at risk. Use Internet resources on home sewage treatment and septic systems to complete the questions below. Refer to the *Laboratory Manual in Physical Geology* home page as needed, **www.prenhall.com/agi**

Questions

26. What are the main purposes of a home septic system?

27. Make a sketch of the relationships among the three parts of a typical septic system listed below. Then add a brief description beside each part to describe its function and purpose.

　a. Septic Tank:

　b. Distribution Box:

　c. Absorption Field (or Drain Field):

28. What information about the bedrock and/or soil is used to determine where to install a properly functioning home septic system?

29. What are some of the common contaminants in groundwater that originate in the wastewater of homes, restaurants, and other businesses?

30. What are the procedures for maintaining a properly functioning home septic system?

Glacial Processes, Landforms, and Indicators of Climate Change

•CONTRIBUTING AUTHORS•

Sharon Laska • *Acadia University*

Kenton E. Strickland • *Wright State University–Lake Campus*

Nancy A. Van Wagoner • *Acadia University*

OBJECTIVES

A. Understand processes of mountain (alpine) glaciation and the landforms and water bodies it produces.

B. Understand processes of continental glaciation and the landforms and water bodies it produces.

C. Construct and analyze topographic profiles of glaciated valleys and infer ice thicknesses.

D. Analyze glacial features and calculate rates of glacial retreat (ablation) in Glacier National Park.

E. Evaluate the use of Nisqually Glacier as a global thermometer for measuring climate change.

MATERIALS

Pencil, eraser, ruler, and pocket stereoscope (optional).

INTRODUCTION

Glaciers are large ice masses that form on land areas that are cold enough and have enough snowfall to sustain them. They form wherever the winter accumulation of snow and ice exceeds the summer ablation (also called *wastage*). *Ablation* (wastage) is the loss of snow and ice by melting and by *sublimation* to gas (direct change from ice to water vapor, without melting). Accumulation commonly occurs in *snowfields*—regions of permanent snow cover (Figure 1).

Glaciers can be divided into two zones, accumulation and ablation (Figure 1). As snow and ice collect in the **zone of accumulation,** they become compacted and highly recrystallized under their own weight. The ice mass then begins to slide and flow downslope like a very viscous (thick) fluid. If you *slowly* squeeze a small piece of ice in the jaws of a vise or pair of pliers, then you can observe how it flows. In nature, glacial ice formed in the zone of accumulation flows downhill into the **zone of ablation,** where it melts or sublimes (undergoes sublimation) faster than new ice can form. The *snowline* is the boundary between the zones of accumulation and ablation. The bottom end of the glacier is the **terminus.**

It helps to understand a glacier by viewing it as a river of ice. The "headwater" is the zone of accumulation, and the "river mouth" is the terminus. Like a river, glaciers *erode* (wear away) rocks, transport their load (tons of rock debris), and deposit their load "downstream" (down-glacier).

The downslope movement and extreme weight of glaciers cause them to abrade and erode (wear away) rock materials that they encounter. They also *pluck* rock material by freezing around it and ripping it from bedrock. The rock debris is then incorporated into the glacial ice and transported many kilometers by the glacier. The debris also gives glacial ice extra abrasive power. As the heavy rock-filled ice moves over the land, it scrapes surfaces like a giant sheet of sandpaper.

Rock debris falling from valley walls commonly accumulates on the surface of a moving glacier and is

From *Laboratory Manual in Physical Geology*, Eighth Edition, American Geological Institute, National Association of Geoscience Teachers, Richard M. Busch, Dennis Tasa. Copyright © 2009 by American Geological Institute. Published by Pearson Prentice Hall. All rights reserved.

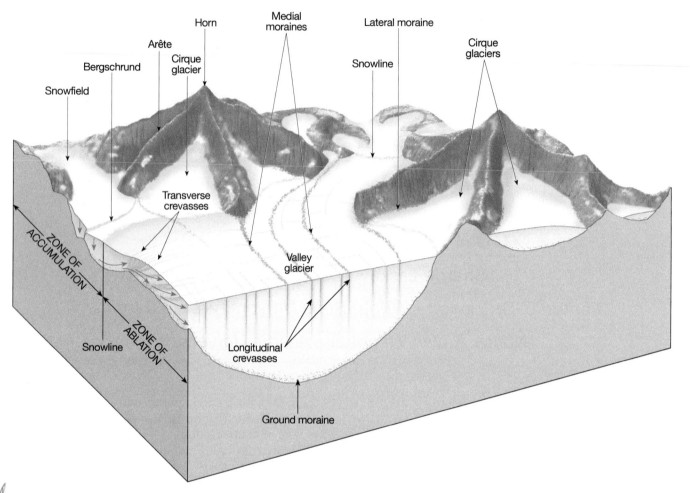

FIGURE 1 Active mountain glaciation, in a hypothetical region. Note cutaway view of glacial ice, showing flow lines and direction (blue lines and arrows).

transported downslope. Thus, glaciers transport huge quantities of sediment, not only *in,* but also *on* the ice.

When a glacier melts, it appears to retreat up the valley from which it flowed. This is called **glacial retreat,** even though the ice is simply melting back (rather than moving back up the hill).

As melting occurs, deposits of rocky gravel, sand, silt, and clay accumulate where there once was ice. These deposits collectively are called **drift.** Drift that accumulates directly from the melting ice is unstratified (unsorted by size) and is called **till.** However, drift that is transported by the meltwater becomes sorted by size, layered, and is called **stratified drift.** Wind also can transport the sand, silt, and clay particles from drift. Wind-transported glacial material can form dunes or *loess* deposits (wind-deposited, unstratified accumulations of clayey silt).

There are four main kinds of glaciers based on their size and form.

- **Cirque glaciers**—small, semicircular to triangular glaciers that form on the sides of mountains.

- **Valley glaciers**—long glaciers that flow down stream valleys in the mountains.

- **Piedmont glaciers**—mergers of two or more valley glaciers at the foot (break in slope) of a mountain range.

- **Ice sheet**—a vast, pancake-shaped ice mound that covers a large portion of a continent and flows independent of the topographic features beneath it. The Antarctic Ice Sheet (covering the entire continent of Antarctica) and Greenland Ice Sheet (covering Greenland) are modern examples.

PART A: GLACIAL PROCESSES AND LANDFORMS

Cirques, valley glaciers, and piedmont glaciers tend to modify mountainous regions of continents, where climatic conditions are sufficient for them to form. Such regions are said to be under the influence of "mountain glaciation" (Figure 1). Ice sheets cover

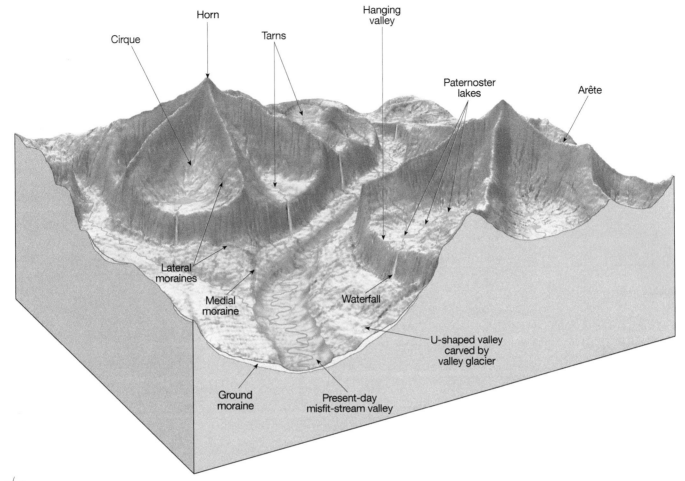

FIGURE 2 The same region as Figure 1, but showing erosion features remaining after total ablation (melting) of glacial ice.

large parts of continents, or even entire continents, which are then said to be under the influence of "continental glaciation."

Mountain Glaciation

Mountain glaciation is characterized by cirque glaciers, valley glaciers, and piedmont glaciers. Poorly developed mountain glaciation involves only cirques, but the best-developed mountain glaciation involves all three types. In some cases, valley and piedmont glaciers are so well developed that only the highest peaks and ridges extend above the ice. Mountain glaciation also is called *alpine glaciation*, because it is the type seen in Europe's Alps.

Figure 1 shows a region with mountain glaciation. Note the extensive *snowfield* in the zone of accumulation. *Snowline* is the elevation above which there is permanent snow cover.

Also note that there are many cracks or fissures in the glacial ice of Figure 1. At the upper end of the glacier is the large *bergschrund* (German, "mountain

crack") that separates the flowing ice from the relatively immobile portion of the snowfield. The other cracks are called **crevasses**—open fissures that form when the velocity of ice flow is variable (such as at bends in valleys). **Transverse crevasses** are perpendicular to the flow direction, and **longitudinal crevasses** are aligned with the direction of flow.

Figure 2 shows the results of mountain glaciation after the glaciers have completely melted. Notice the characteristic landforms, water bodies, and sedimentary deposits.

For your convenience, distinctive features of glacial lands are summarized in three figures:

- *erosional* features in Figure 3
- *depositional* features in Figure 4
- *water bodies* in Figure 5.

Note that some features are identical in mountain glaciation and continental glaciation, but others are unique to one or the other. Study the descriptions in

EROSIONAL FEATURES OF GLACIATED REGIONS		MOUNTAIN GLACIATION	CONTINENTAL GLACIATION
Cirque	Bowl-shaped depression on a high mountain slope, formed by a cirque glacier	X	
Arête	Sharp, jagged, knife-edge ridge between two cirques or glaciated valleys	X	
Col	Mountain pass formed by the headward erosion of cirques	X	
Horn	Steep-sided, pyramid-shaped peak produced by headward erosion of several cirques	X	
Headwall	Steep slope or rock cliff at the upslope end of a glaciated valley or cirque	X	
Glacial trough	U-shaped, steep-walled, glaciated valley formed by the scouring action of a valley glacier	X	
Hanging valley	Glacial trough of a tributary glacier, elevated above the main trough	X	
Roche moutonnée	Asymmetrical knoll or small hill of bedrock, formed by glacial abrasion on the smooth stoss side (side from which the glacier came) and by plucking (prying and pulling by glacial ice) on the less-smooth lee side (down-glacier side)		X
Glacial striations and grooves	Parallel linear scratches and grooves in bedrock surfaces, resulting from glacial scouring	X	X
Glacial polish	Smooth bedrock surfaces caused by glacial abrasion (sanding action of glaciers analogous to sanding of wood with sandpaper)	X	X

FIGURE 3 Erosional features produced by mountain or continental glaciation.

these three figures and compare them with the visuals in Figures 1 and 2.

Continental Glaciation

During the Pleistocene Epoch, or "Ice Age," that ended approximately 10,000 years ago, thick ice sheets covered most of Canada, large parts of Alaska, and the northern contiguous United States. These continental glaciers produced a variety of characteristic landforms (Figure 6, Figure 7).

Recognizing and interpreting these landforms is important in conducting work such as regional soil analyses, studies of surface drainage and water supply, and exploration for sources of sand, gravel, and minerals. The thousands of lakes in the Precambrian Shield area of Canada also are a legacy of this continental glaciation, as are the fertile soils of the north-central United States and south-central Canada.

Questions

1. In Figure 8, examine the typical stream cobble and typical glacial cobble. Explain how you think the two different physical-abrasion processes (river abrasion versus glacial abrasion) can produce such different-looking cobbles.

DEPOSITIONAL FEATURES OF GLACIATED REGIONS		MOUNTAIN GLACIATION	CONTINENTAL GLACIATION
Ground moraine	Sheetlike layer (blanket) of till left on the landscape by a receding (wasting) glacier.	X	X
Terminal moraine	Ridge of till that formed along the leading edge of the farthest advance of a glacier.	X	X
Recessional moraine	Ridge of till that forms at terminus of a glacier, behind (up-glacier) and generally parallel to the terminal moraine; formed during a temporary halt (stand) in recession of a wasting glacier.	X	X
Lateral moraine	A body of rock fragments at or within the side of a valley glacier where it touches bedrock and scours the rock fragments from the side of the valley. It is visible along the sides of the glacier and on its surface in its ablation zone. When the glacier melts, the lateral moraine will remain as a nerrow ridge of till or boulder train on the side of the valley.	X	
Medial moraine	A long narrow body of rock fragments carried in or upon the middle of a valley glacier and parallel to its sides, usually formed by the merging of lateral moraines from two or more merging valley glaciers. It is visible on the surface of the glacier in its ablation zone. When the glaciers melt, the medial moraine will remain as a narrow ridge of till or boulder train in the middle of the valley.	X	
Drumlin	An elongated mound or ridge of glacial till (unstratified drift) that accumulated under a glacier and was elongated and streamlined by movement (flow) of the glacier. Its long axis is parallel to ice flow. It normally has a blunt end in the direction from which the ice came and long narrow tail in the direction that the ice was flowing.		X
Kame	A low mound, knob, or short irregular ridge of stratified drift (sand and gravel) sorted by and deposited from meltwater flowing a short distance beneath, within, or on top of a glacier. When the ice melted, the kame remained.		X
Esker	Long, narrow, sinuous ridge of stratified drift deposited by meltwater streams flowing under glacial ice or in tunnels within the glacial ice		X
Erratic	Boulder or smaller fragment of rock resting far from its source on bedrock of a different type.	X	X
Boulder train	A line or band of boulders and smaller rock clasts (cobbles, gravel, sand) transported by a glacier (often for many kilometers) and extending from the bedrock source where they originated to the place where the glacier carried them. When deposited on different bedrock, the rocks are called erratics.	X	X
Outwash	Stratified drift (mud, sand and gravel) transported, sorted, and deposited by meltwater streams (usually muddy braided streams) flowing in front of (down-slope from) the terminus of the melting glacier.	X	X
Outwash plain	Plain formed by blanket-like deposition of outwash; usually an outwash braid plain, formed by the coalescence of many braided streams having their origins along a common glacial terminus.	X	X
Valley train	Long, narrow sheet of outwash (outwash braid plain of one braided stream, or floodplain of a meandering stream) that extends far beyond the terminus of a glacier.	X	
Beach line	Landward edge of a shoreline of a lake formed from damming of glacial meltwater, or temporary ponding of glacial meltwater in a topographic depression.		X
Glacial-lake deposits	Layers of sediment in the lake bed, deltas, or beaches of a glacial lake.		X
Loess	Unstratified sheets of clayey silt and silty clay transported beyond the margins of a glacier by wind and/or braided streams; it is compact and able to resist significant erosion when exposed in steep slopes or cliffs.		X

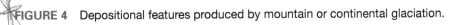

FIGURE 4 Depositional features produced by mountain or continental glaciation.

127

WATER BODIES OF GLACIATED REGIONS		MOUNTAIN GLACIATION	CONTINENTAL GLACIATION
Tarn	Small lake in a cirque (bowl-shaped depression formed by a cirque glacier). A melting cirque glacier may also fill part of the cirque and may be in direct contact with or slightly up-slope from the tarn.	X	
Ice-dammed lake	Lake formed brhind a mass of ice sheets and blocks that have wedged together and blocked the flow of water from a melting glacier and or river. Such natural dams may burst and produce a catastropic flood of water, ice blocks, and sediment.	X	X
Paternoster lakes	Chain of small lakes in a glacial trough.	X	
Finger lake	Long narrow lake in a glacial trough that was cut into bedrock by the scouring action of glacial ice (containing rock particles and acting like sand paper as it flows downhill) and usually dammed by a deposit of glacial gravel (end or recessional moraine).	X	X
Kettle lake or kettle hole	Small lake or water-saturated depression (10s to 1000s of meters wide) in glacial drift, formed by melting of an isolated, detached block of ice left behind by a glacier in retreat (melting back) or buried in outwash from a flood caused by the collapse of an ice-dammed lake.	X	X
Swale	Narrow marsh, swamp, or very shallow lake in a long shallow depression between two moraines.		X
Marginal glacial lake	Lake formed at the margin (edge) of a glacier as a result of accumulating meltwater; the upslope edge of the lake is the melting glacier itself.	X	X
Meltwater stream	Stream of water derived from melting glacial ice, that flows under the ice, on the ice, along the margins of the ice, or beyond the margins of the ice.	X	X
Misfit stream	Stream that is not large enough and powerful enough to have cut the valley it occupies. The valley must have been cut at a time when the stream was larger and had more cutting power or else it was cut by another process such as scouring by glacial ice.	X	X
Marsh or swamp	Saturated, poorly drained areas that are permanently or intermittently covered with water and have grassy vegetation (swamp) or shrubs and trees (marsh).	X	X

FIGURE 5 Water bodies produced as a result of mountain or continental glaciation.

Refer to the Siffleur River, Alberta, quadrangle (Figure 9) for these questions:

2. What is the name given to features like Marmot Mountain and Conical Peak? How do such features form?

3. The boundary between Improvement Districts 9 and 10 follows a ridge from the Siffleur River Valley to Mount Kentigern. What type of ridge is this, and how did it form?

4. Near the northern edge of the map, what type of valley is located above the falls west of the Siffleur River, and how did it form?

5. What type of lake is at the headwaters of the stream that forms these falls?

6. What other features produced by mountain glaciation can you see on this map?

Refer to Figure 10, a portion of the Anchorage (B-2), Alaska, quadrangle, for the following questions. In the southwestern corner, note the Harvard Arm of Prince William Sound. The famous *Exxon Valdez* oil spill occurred just south of this area (it did not affect Harvard Arm).

7. Lateral and medial moraines in/on the ablation zone of Harvard Glacier are indicated by the

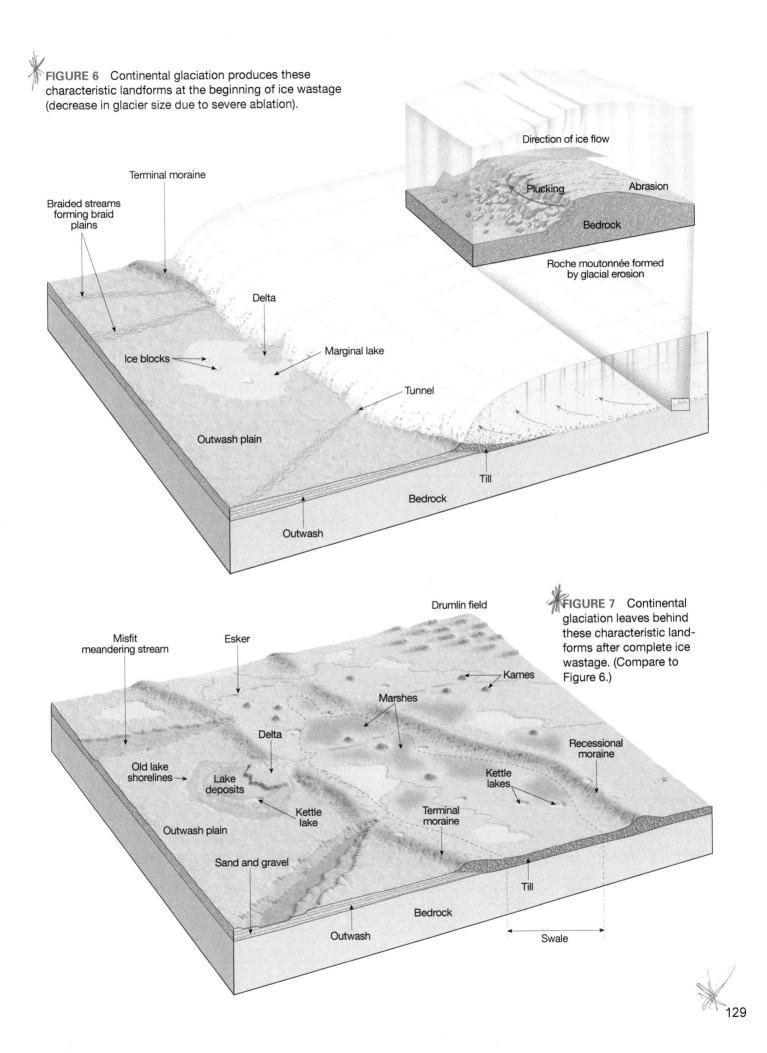

FIGURE 6 Continental glaciation produces these characteristic landforms at the beginning of ice wastage (decrease in glacier size due to severe ablation).

Direction of ice flow

Plucking

Abrasion

Bedrock

Roche moutonnée formed by glacial erosion

Terminal moraine

Braided streams forming braid plains

Delta

Ice blocks

Marginal lake

Tunnel

Outwash plain

Till

Outwash

Bedrock

FIGURE 7 Continental glaciation leaves behind these characteristic land-forms after complete ice wastage. (Compare to Figure 6.)

Drumlin field

Misfit meandering stream

Esker

Kames

Marshes

Delta

Recessional moraine

Old lake shorelines

Lake deposits

Kettle lakes

Kettle lake

Outwash plain

Terminal moraine

Sand and gravel

Till

Outwash

Bedrock

Swale

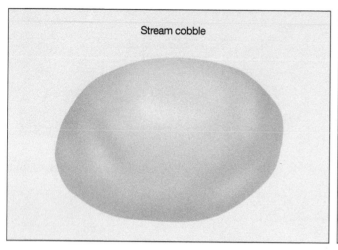
Stream cobble

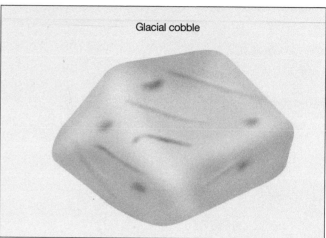
Glacial cobble

FIGURE 8 Note the differences between a stream cobble and a glacial cobble. Stream cobbles are rounded to well-rounded and have smooth surfaces. Glacial cobbles are angular or faceted and have many scratch marks. (A cobble is a clast between a pebble and a boulder in size, 64–256 mm diameter.)

brown stippled (finely dotted) pattern. If a hiker found gold in rock fragments on the glacier at location **C**, then would you look for gold near location **X, Y,** or **Z**? Explain your reasoning.

8. Notice the crevasses within a mile of Harvard Glacier's terminus. What specific kind of crevasses are they, and why do you think they formed only on this part of the glacier?

9. Between the Harvard and Yale glaciers, notice how the Dora Keen Range has been shaped by these two main glaciers and thins to the southwest. How could you use this information to infer how ice has flowed in regions where glaciers are no longer present?

Refer to Figure 11, part of the Peterborough, Ontario, quadrangle, for the following questions. This area lies north of Lake Ontario.

10. Study the size and shape of the short, oblong rounded hills. Fieldwork has revealed that they are made of till. What type of feature are they and how did they form?

11. Using a ruler, draw a line on ten of the oblong hills of question 10 to indicate their long axis. In what direction did glaciers move (advance toward) in this area? Explain.

12. Find the red highway, Route 7, that crosses the northern part of the map. About 1 mile south of the circled number 7 that identifies Route 7, there is the long, narrow, sinuous hill that runs northeast from the pale blue number 36. What would you call this feature, and how do you think it formed?

13. Imagine that you could visit the feature in question 12 and dig through it with a bulldozer. What would you expect to find inside of the feature (be as exact as you can)?

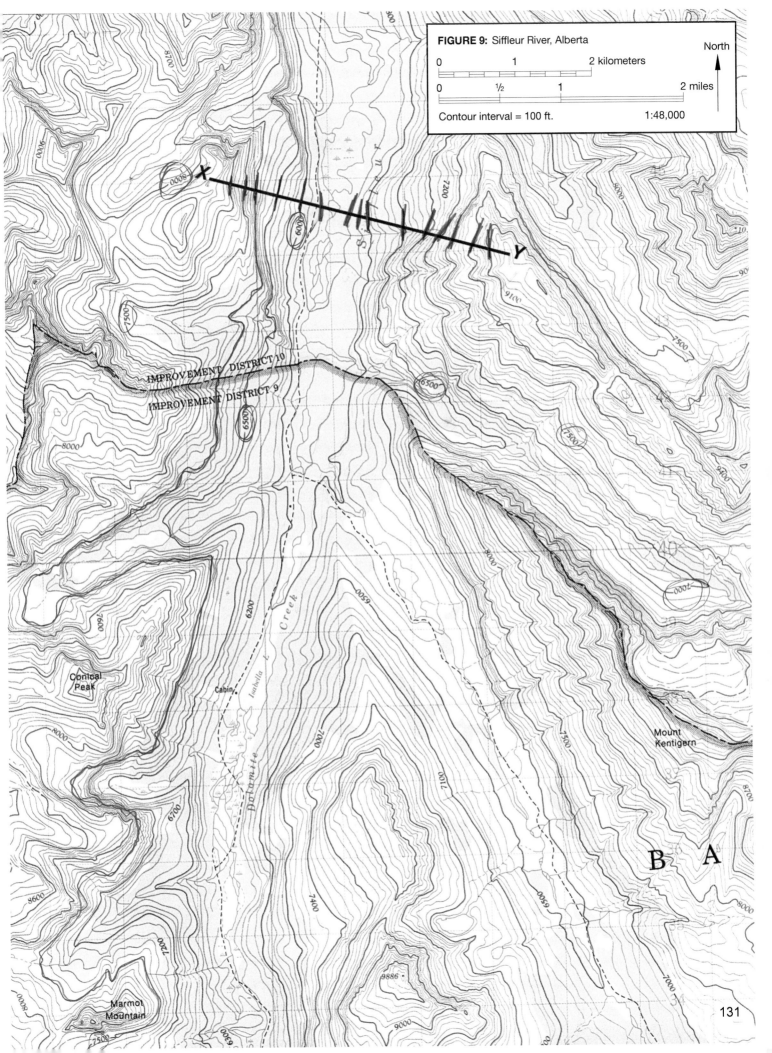

FIGURE 9: Siffleur River, Alberta

North

0   1   2 kilometers

0   ½   1   2 miles

Contour interval = 100 ft.   1:48,000

X

Y

IMPROVEMENT DISTRICT 10

IMPROVEMENT DISTRICT 9

Isabella Creek

Dolomite Creek

Conical Peak

Cabin

Mount Kentigern

Marmot Mountain

B   A

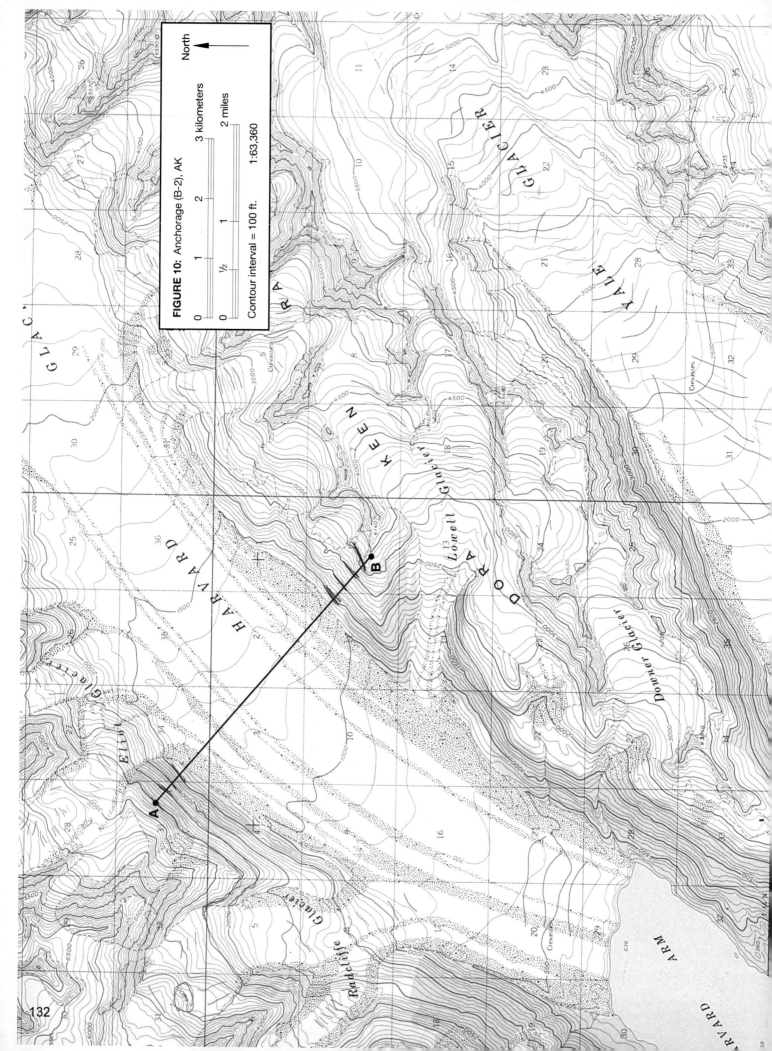

FIGURE 10: Anchorage (B-2), AK

North

3 kilometers

2 miles

0   1   2   3 kilometers

0   ½   1   2 miles

Contour interval = 100 ft.   1:63,360

FIGURE 11: Peterborough, Ontario

Contour interval = 25 ft.

1:48,000

North

PART B: GLACIATION IN WISCONSIN

The most recent glaciation of Earth is called the *Wisconsinan glaciation,* named for the state of Wisconsin, where it left behind many erosional and depositional features. The Wisconsinan glaciation reached its maximum development about 18,000 years ago, when a *Laurentide ice sheet* covered central and eastern Canada, the Great Lakes Region, and the northeastern United States. It ended by about 10,000 years ago, at the start of the recent interglaciation (Recent or Holocene Epoch).

Refer to Figure 12, a portion of the Whitewater, Wisconsin, quadrangle and Figure 13, the accompanying stereogram, for these questions:

Questions

14. List the features of glaciated regions from Figures 3 and 4 that are present in this region.

15. Based on your answer to Question 14 and the information provided above, what kind of glaciation (mountain versus continental) has shaped this landscape?

16. Describe what direction the ice flowed over this region. Cite evidence for your inference.

17. What kinds of lakes are present in this region, and how did they form? (Refer to Figure 5.)

18. In the southeastern corner of the map, the forested area is probably what kind of feature?

19. Note the swampy and marshy area running from the west-central edge of the map to the northeastern corner. Describe the probable origin of this feature (more than one answer is possible).

PART C: COMPARING TOPOGRAPHIC PROFILES OF GLACIATED VALLEYS

Questions

20. Complete the topographic profile on the left-hand side of Figure 14 for line **X–Y,** *across the Siffleur River Valley.*

    a. What is the vertical exaggeration of this topographic profile?

    b. Is this a normal profile for a river valley? Why?

    c. Why does the Siffleur River Valley have this shape?

21. On the right-hand side of Figure 14, complete the topographic profile for line **A–B** *across the Harvard Glacier.*

    a. What is the vertical exaggeration of this topographic profile?

    b. Label the part of the profile that is the top surface of the glacier.

    c. Using a dashed line draw where you think the rock bottom of the valley is located under the Harvard Glacier. (Your drawing may extend slightly below the figure.)

22. Based on your work in Questions 20 and 21, what is the maximum thickness of Harvard Glacier at line **A–B**? Explain your reasoning.

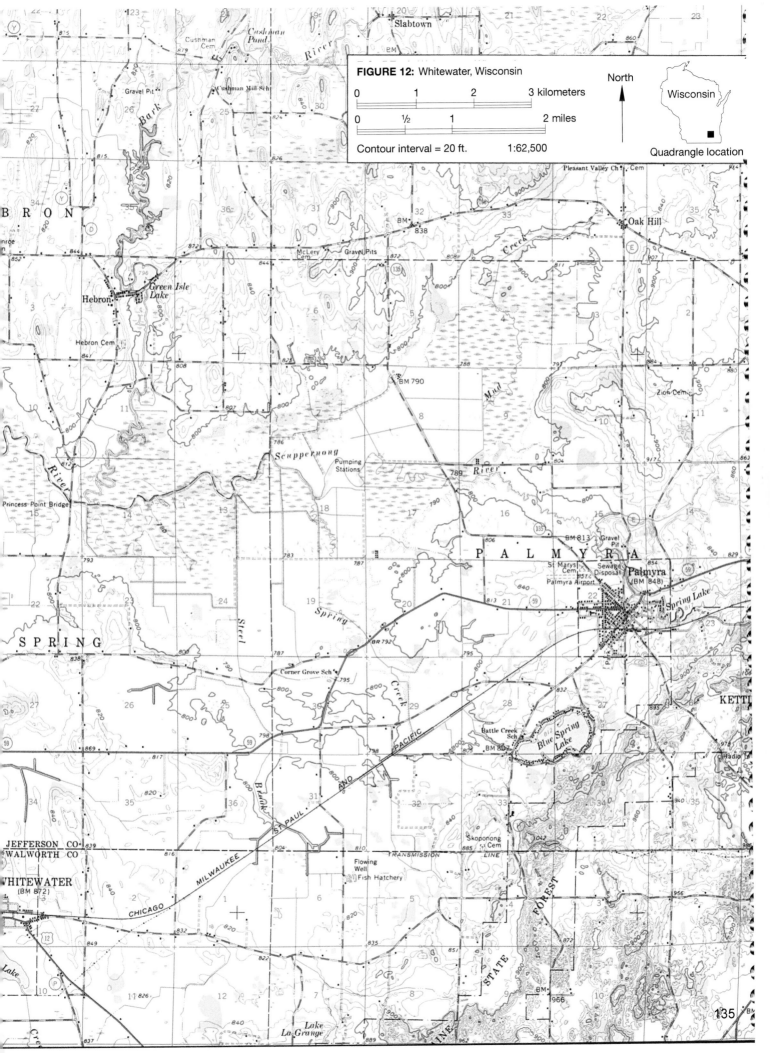

FIGURE 12: Whitewater, Wisconsin

0   1   2   3 kilometers

0   ½   1   2 miles

Contour interval = 20 ft.   1:62,500

North

Wisconsin

Quadrangle location

135

FIGURE 13 National high-altitude photograph (NHAP, color-infrared) stereogram of the Whitewater, Wisconsin, region. View the stereogram using a pocket stereoscope and compare it to Figure 12.   (Courtesy of U.S. Geological Survey)

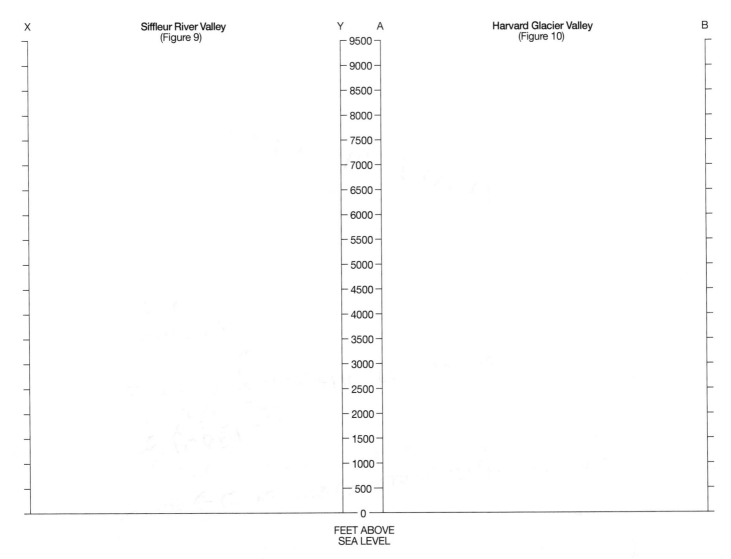

FIGURE 14 Graphs for completing topographic profiles of glaciated valleys (Part C).

PART D: GLACIER NATIONAL PARK, MONTANA

Glacier National Park is located on the northern edge of Montana, across the border from Alberta and British Columbia, Canada. Most of the erosional features formed by glaciation in the park were formed during the Wisconsinan glaciation that ended about 10,000 years ago. Today, only small cirque glaciers exist in the park. Thirty-seven of them are named, and nine of those can be observed on the topographic map of part of the park in Figure 15. Use the map and chart of glacier data in Figure 15 to answer the following questions.

Questions

23. List the features of glaciated regions from Figures 3 and 4 that are present in this region.

24. Locate Quartz Lake and Middle Quartz Lake in the southwest part of the map. Notice the Patrol Cabin located between these lakes. Describe the chain of geologic/glacial events (steps) that led to formation of Quartz Lake, the valley of Quartz Lake, the small piece of land on which the Patrol Cabin is located, and the cirque in which Rainbow Glacier is located today.

25. Based on your answers to Questions 23 and 24, what kind of glaciation (mountain versus continental) has shaped this landscape?

26. Locate the Continental Divide and think of ways that it may be related to weather and climate in the region. Recall that weather systems generally move across the United States from west to east.

    a. Describe how modern glaciers of this region are distributed in relation to the Continental Divide.

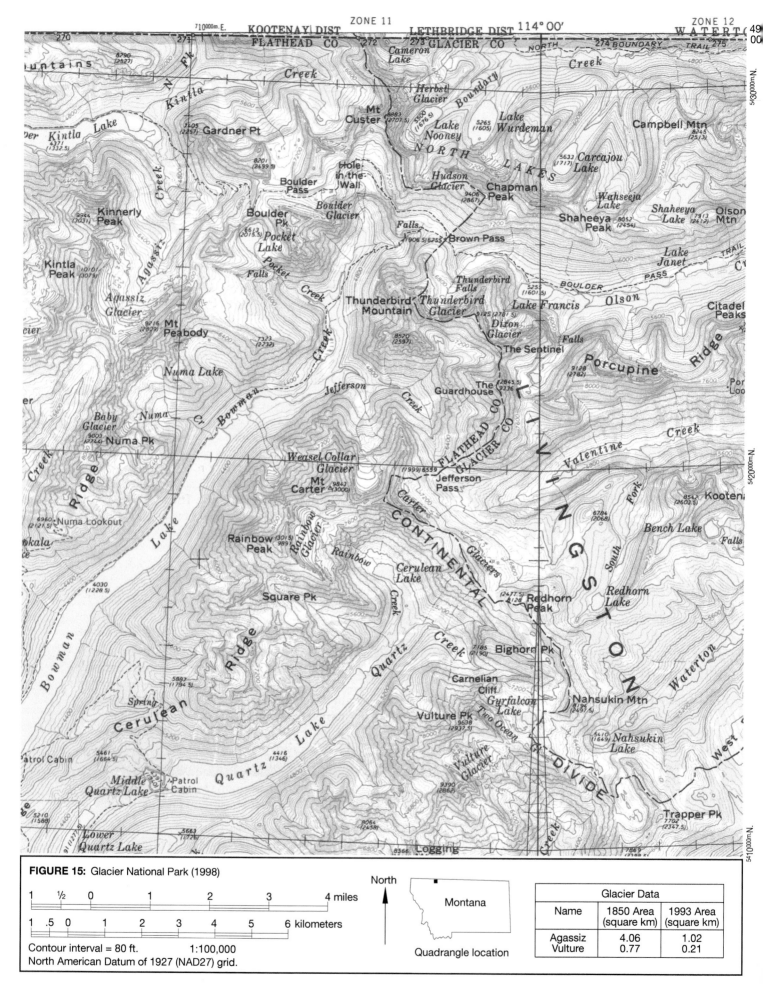

FIGURE 15: Glacier National Park (1998)

North

Montana

Quadrangle location

Contour interval = 80 ft.   1:100,000
North American Datum of 1927 (NAD27) grid.

Glacier Data		
Name	1850 Area (square km)	1993 Area (square km)
Agassiz	4.06	1.02
Vulture	0.77	0.21

138

b. Based on the distribution you observed, describe the weather/climate conditions that may exist on opposite sides of the Continental Divide in this region.

27. By what percentage did each of the glaciers below decrease in size between 1850 and 1993?

   a. Agassiz Glacier:

   b. Vulture Glacier:

28. What was the rate, in km^2/yr, that each of the glaciers receded between 1850 and 1993?

   a. Agassiz Glacier:

   b. Vulture Glacier:

29. Based on the rates you calculated in Question 28, calculate the year in which each of these glaciers will be completely melted.

   a. Agassiz Glacier:

   b. Vulture Glacier:

30. The largest glacier in Figure 15, and one of the largest in Glacier National Park, is Rainbow Glacier. Predict what year Rainbow Glacier will be completely melted (based on your calculations in Question 28 and assuming no significant change in climate). Explain your reasoning and calculation.

PART E: NISQUALLY GLACIER— A GLOBAL THERMOMETER?

Nisqually Glacier is one of many active valley glaciers that occupy the radial drainage of Mt. Rainier—an active volcano located near Seattle, Washington, in the Cascade Range of the western United States. Nisqually Glacier occurs on the southern side of Mt. Rainier and flows south toward the Nisqually River Bridge in Figure 16. The position of the glacier's terminus (downhill end) was first recorded in 1857, and it has been measured and mapped by numerous geologists since that time. The map in Figure 16 was prepared by the U.S. Geological Survey in 1976 and shows where the terminus of Nisqually Glacier was located at various times from 1840 to 1997. (The 1994 and 1997 positions were added for this laboratory, based on NHAP aerial photographs and satellite imagery.) Notice how the glacier has more or less retreated up the valley since 1840. Measure, chart, graph, and analyze this retreat below.

Questions

31. Fill in the Nisqually Glacier Data Chart on the left side of Figure 17. To do this, use a ruler and the map's bar scale to measure the distance in kilometers from Nisqually River Bridge to the position of the glacier's terminus (red dot) for each year of the chart. Be sure to record your distance measurements to two decimal points (hundredths of kilometers).

32. Plot your data from Question 31 (Nisqually Glacier Data Chart) in the graph on the right side of Figure 17. After plotting each point of data, connect the dots with a smooth, light pencil line. Notice that the glacier terminus retreated up-valley at some times, but advanced back down the valley at other times. Summarize these changes in a chart or paragraph, relative to specific years of the data.

33. Notice the blue and red graph of climatic data at the bottom of Figure 17 provided by the NOAA National Climatic Data Center (NCDC). NCDC's global mean temperatures are mean temperatures for Earth calculated by processing data from thousands of observation sites throughout the world (from 1880 to 2005). The temperature data were corrected for factors such as increase in temperature around urban centers and decrease in temperature with elevation. Although NCDC collects and processes data on land and sea, this graph only shows the variation in annually averaged global land surface temperature since 1880.

   a. Describe the long-term trend in this graph—how averaged global land surface temperature changed from 1880 to 2005.

   b. Lightly in pencil, trace any shorter-term pattern of cyclic climate change that you can identify in the graph. Describe this cyclic shorter-term trend.

34. Describe how the changes in position of the terminus of Nisqually Glacier compare to variations in annually averaged global land surface temperature. Be as specific as you can.

35. Based on all of your work above, do you think Nisqually Glacier can be used as a global thermometer for measuring climate change? Explain.

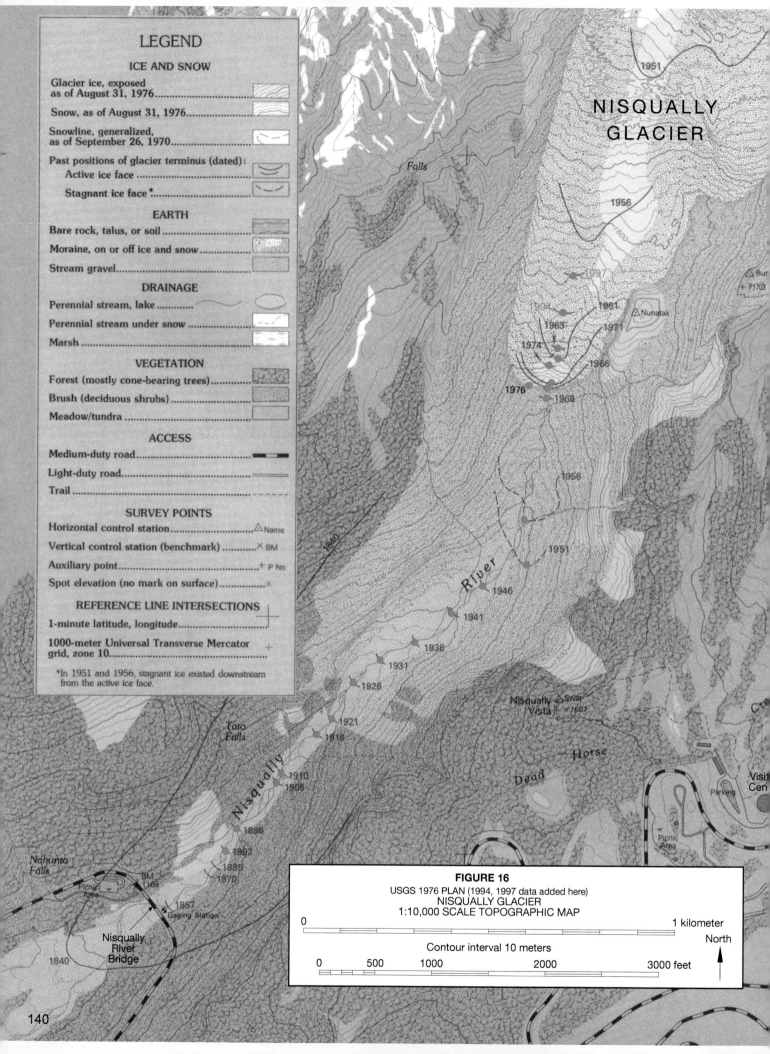

LEGEND

ICE AND SNOW

Glacier ice, exposed
as of August 31, 1976..............

Snow, as of August 31, 1976.............

Snowline, generalized,
as of September 26, 1970.............

Past positions of glacier terminus (dated):
  Active ice face ....
  Stagnant ice face *.............

EARTH

Bare rock, talus, or soil ....

Moraine, on or off ice and snow ....

Stream gravel.............

DRAINAGE

Perennial stream, lake ....

Perennial stream under snow ....

Marsh ....

VEGETATION

Forest (mostly cone-bearing trees).............

Brush (deciduous shrubs).............

Meadow/tundra ....

ACCESS

Medium-duty road.............

Light-duty road.............

Trail ....

SURVEY POINTS

Horizontal control station.............△Name

Vertical control station (benchmark) ....× BM

Auxiliary point.............+ P No

Spot elevation (no mark on surface).............×

REFERENCE LINE INTERSECTIONS

1-minute latitude, longitude.............

1000-meter Universal Transverse Mercator
grid, zone 10.............

*In 1951 and 1956, stagnant ice existed downstream
from the active ice face.

NISQUALLY
GLACIER

Falls

1951

1956

1997

1994   1961

1963   1971

1974

1966

1976   1968

Nunatak

Bur

P1703

1956

1951

1946

1941

1936

River

1931

1926

1921

1916

Tato
Falls

1910
1905

Nisqually

1898

1892

1885
1870

Nahunta
Falls

Picnic
Area

BM
1169

1857
Gaging Station

Nisqually
River
Bridge

1840

Nisqually
Vista   Swa
×1601

Dead   Horse   Cre

Parking   Visi
Cen

Picnic
Area

FIGURE 16
USGS 1976 PLAN (1994, 1997 data added here)
NISQUALLY GLACIER
1:10,000 SCALE TOPOGRAPHIC MAP

0   1 kilometer

North

Contour interval 10 meters

0   500   1000   2000   3000 feet

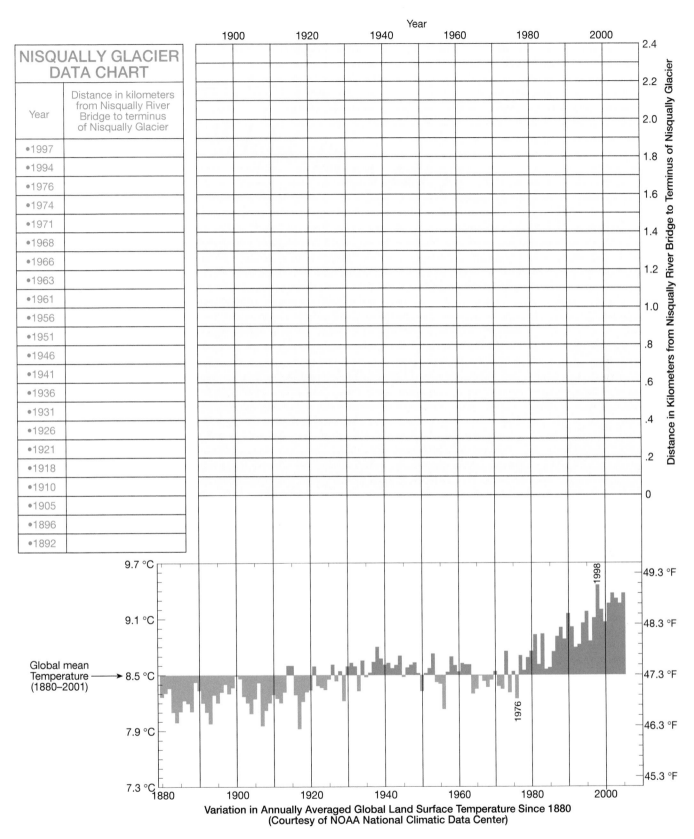

NISQUALLY GLACIER DATA CHART	
Year	Distance in kilometers from Nisqually River Bridge to terminus of Nisqually Glacier
•1997	
•1994	
•1976	
•1974	
•1971	
•1968	
•1966	
•1963	
•1961	
•1956	
•1951	
•1946	
•1941	
•1936	
•1931	
•1926	
•1921	
•1918	
•1910	
•1905	
•1896	
•1892	

Variation in Annually Averaged Global Land Surface Temperature Since 1880
(Courtesy of NOAA National Climatic Data Center)

FIGURE 17 Graph of changes in position of the terminus of Nisqually Glacier compared to the variation in annually averaged global land surface temperature since 1880 (Part E).

Coastal Processes, Landforms, Hazards, and Risks

•CONTRIBUTING AUTHORS•

James G. Titus • *U.S. Environmental Protection Agency*

Donald W. Watson • *Slippery Rock University*

OBJECTIVES

A. Identify and interpret natural shoreline landforms.

B. Distinguish between emergent and submergent shorelines.

C. Know the common types of artificial structures that are used to modify shorelines and understand their effects on coastal environments.

D. Be aware of the probability of global sea-level rise and the coastal hazards and increased risks that this sea-level rise may cause.

MATERIALS

Pencils, eraser, ruler, set of colored pencils, and pocket stereoscope.

INTRODUCTION

The shorelines of lakes and oceans are among the most rapidly changing parts of the Earth's surface. All coastlines are subject to *erosion* (wearing away) by waves. A coastline comprised of loose sediment can be eroded easily and rapidly. A coastline composed of dense bedrock or plastic-like mud erodes much more slowly.

Several factors determine the characteristic landforms of shorelines. They include the shape of the shoreline, the materials that comprise the shoreline (rock, plastic mud, loose sediment, concrete), the source and supply of sediments, the direction that currents move along the shoreline, and the effects of major storms.

Most coastlines also are affected by changes in mean (average) sea level:

- A *rising* sea level creates a **submergent coastline**—one that is flooding and receding (*retrogradational*). Sea level rise is caused either by the water level actually rising (called *transgression*), or by the land getting lower (called *subsidence*).

- A *falling* sea level creates an **emergent coastline**—one that is being elevated above sea level and building out into the water (*progradational*). Sea level fall is caused either by the water level actually falling (called *regression*), or by rising of the land (called *uplift*).

Submergent coastlines may display some emergent features, and vice versa. For example, the Louisiana coastline is submergent, enough so that dikes and levees have been built to keep the ocean from flooding New Orleans. However, the Mississippi Delta is progradational—building out into the water—a feature of most emergent coastlines. It is progradational because of the vast supply of sediment being carried there and deposited by the Mississippi River.

Thus, *sediment supply* is a major factor in determining whether a coastline is progradational or retrogradational, regardless of vertical changes of land level or water level.

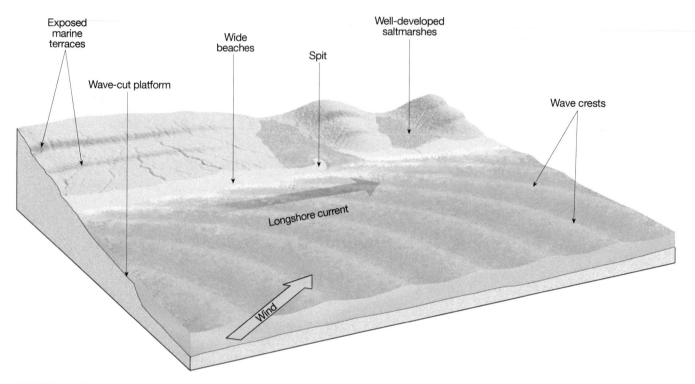

FIGURE 1 *Emergent* coastline features. An emergent coastline is caused by sea-level lowering, the land rising, or both. Emergence causes tidal flats and coastal wetlands to expand, wave-cut terraces are exposed to view, deltas prograde at faster rates, and wide stable beaches develop.

Sediment transport and the effects of major storms also are very important agents of shoreline change. A single storm can completely change the form of a coastline.

Figures 1 and 2 illustrate some features of *emergent* and *submergent* shorelines. Study these features and their definitions below.

- **Barrier island**—a long, narrow island that parallels the mainland coastline and is separated from the mainland by a lagoon, tidal flat, or salt marsh.

- **Beach**—a gently sloping deposit of sand or gravel along the edge of a shoreline.

- **Berm crest**—the highest part of a beach; it separates the *foreshore* (seaward part of the shoreline) from the *backshore* (landward part of the shoreline).

- **Washover fan**—a fan-shaped deposit of sand or gravel transported and deposited landward of the beach during a storm or very high tide.

- **Estuary**—a river valley flooded by a rise in the level of an ocean or lake. (A flooded glacial valley is called a *fjord*.)

- **Longshore current**—a water current in the *surf zone* (zone where waves break). It flows slowly parallel to shoreline, driven by waves that were caused by wind.

- **Delta**—a sediment deposit at the mouth of a river where it enters an ocean or lake.

- **Headland**—projection of land that extends into an ocean or lake and generally has cliffs along its water boundary.

- **Spit**—a sand bar extending from the end of a beach into the mouth of an adjacent bay.

- **Tidal flat**—muddy or sandy area that is covered with water at high tide and exposed at low tide.

- **Saltmarsh**—a marsh that is flooded by ocean water at high tide.

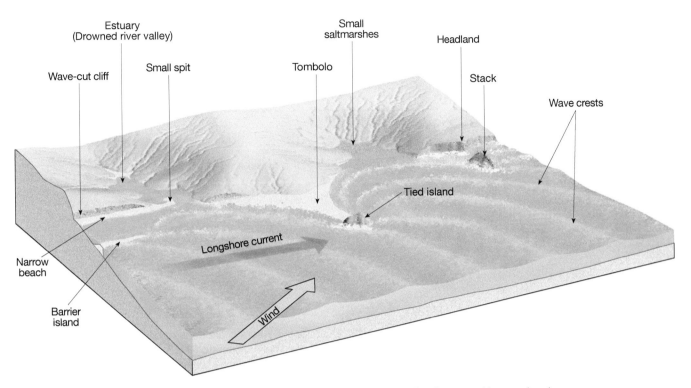

FIGURE 2 *Submergent* (drowning) coastline features. A submergent coastline is caused by sea-level rising (transgression), sinking of the land, or both. As the land is flooded, the waves cut cliffs, valleys are flooded to form estuaries, wetlands are submerged, deep bays develop, beaches narrow, and islands are created.

- **Wave-cut cliff** (or *sea cliff*)—seaward-facing cliff along a steep shoreline, produced by wave erosion.

- **Wave-cut platform**—a bench or shelf at sea level (or lake level) along a steep shore, and formed by wave erosion.

- **Marine terrace**—an elevated platform that is bounded on its seaward side by a cliff or steep slope (and formed when a wave-cut platform is elevated by uplift or regression).

- **Stack**—an isolated rocky island near a headland cliff.

- **Tombolo**—a sand bar that connects an island with the mainland or another island.

- **Tied island**—an island connected to the mainland or another island by a tombolo.

Humans build several common types of coastal structures in order to protect harbors, build up sandy beaches, or extend the shoreline. Study these four kinds of structures and their effects both in Figure 3 and below.

- **Sea wall**—an embankment of boulders, reinforced concrete, or other material constructed against a shoreline to prevent erosion by waves and currents.

- **Breakwater**—an offshore wall constructed parallel to a shoreline to break waves. The longshore current is halted behind such walls, so the sand accumulates there and the beach widens. Where the breakwater is used to protect a harbor from currents and waves, sand often collects behind the breakwater and may have to be dredged.

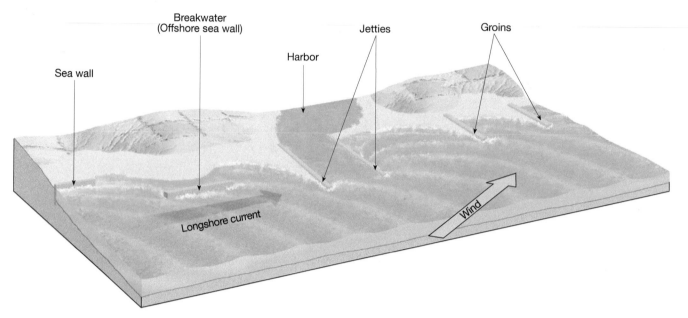

FIGURE 3 Coastal structures—sea walls, breakwaters, groins, and jetties. **Sea walls** are constructed along the shore to stop erosion of the shore or extend the shoreline (as sediment is used to fill in behind them). **Breakwaters** are a type of offshore sea wall constructed parallel to shoreline. The breakwaters stop waves from reaching the beach, so the longshore drift is broken and sand accumulates behind them (instead of being carried down shore with the longshore current). **Groins** are short walls constructed perpendicular to shore. They trap sand on the side from which the longshore current is carrying sand against them. **Jetties** are long walls constructed at entrances to harbors to keep waves from entering the harbors. However, they also trap sand just like groins.

- **Groin** (or *groyne*)—a short wall constructed perpendicular to shoreline in order to trap sand and make or build up a beach. Sand accumulates on the up-current side of the groin in relation to the longshore current.

- **Jetties**—long walls extending from shore at the mouths of harbors and used to protect the harbor entrance from filling with sand or being eroded by waves and currents. Jetties are usually constructed of boulders and in pairs (one on each side of a harbor or inlet).

PART A: DYNAMIC NATURAL COASTLINES

Refer to the Space Shuttle photograph of the Po Delta, Italy (Figure 4). The city of Adria, on the Po River in northern Italy, was a thriving seaport during Etruscan times (600 B.C.). Adria had such fame as to give its name to the Adriatic Sea, the gulf into which the Po River flows. Over the years, the Po River has deposited sediment at its mouth in the Po Delta. Because of the Po Delta's progradation, Adria is no longer located on the shoreline of the Adriatic Sea. The modern shoreline is far downstream from Adria.

Questions

1. What has been the average annual rate of Po Delta progradation in centimeters per year (cm/yr) since Adria was a thriving seaport on the coastline of the Adriatic Sea?

2. Based on the average annual rate calculated in Question 1, how many centimeters would the Po Delta prograde during the lifetime of someone who lived to be 60 years old?

FIGURE 4 Space Shuttle photograph of the Po Delta region, northern Italy. (Courtesy of NASA)

Refer to the Oceanside, California, quadrangle (Figure 5) and complete Questions 3 and 4.

3. If you climb inland from the Pacific Ocean at South Oceanside to Fire Mountain, you will cross a series of relatively flat surfaces located at successively higher elevations and separated by steep hills or cliffs. All together, they resemble a sort of giant staircase.

   a. About how many of these coastal features are there?

   b. What are the approximate elevations of the flat surfaces, from lowest to highest?

   c. What are these coastal features called, and what is their probable origin?

4. Is this a coastline of emergence or of submergence? Why?

Refer to the Point Reyes, California, quadrangle (Figure 6). Point Reyes is a subtriangular landmass bounded on the west by the Pacific Ocean, on the south by Drakes Bay, and on the east by the San Andreas Fault. The fault runs along Sir Francis Drake Road in the northeast corner of the map.

5. Which area is *more* resistant to wave erosion: Point Reyes or Point Reyes Beach? Why?

6. How did Drakes Estero (Spanish: "estuary") form?

7. What is the direction of longshore drift in Drakes Bay? How can you tell?

8. If a groin was constructed from Limantour Spit, at the "n" in Limantour, then on what side of the groin would sand accumulate (east or west)? Why?

9. Is this a coastline of emergence or submergence? Explain.

147

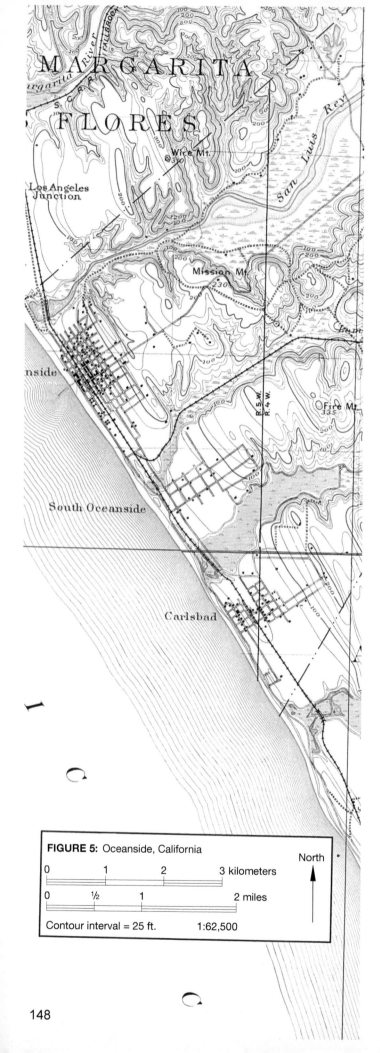

Refer to the map and photographs of Saint Catherines Island, Georgia (Figure 7). Note that on the east-central portion of the island there is a large area of saltmarsh mud. Living saltmarsh plants are present there, as shown on the right (west) in Figures 7A and B. Also, note the linear sandy beach in Figures 7A and B, bounded on its seaward side (left) by another strip of saltmarsh mud. However, all of the living, surficial saltmarsh plants and animals have been stripped from this area. This is called **relict** saltmarsh mud (mud remaining from an ancient saltmarsh).

10. What type of sediment is probably present beneath the beach sands in Figures 7A and B?

11. Explain how you think the beach sands became located landward of the relict saltmarsh mud.

12. Portions of the living saltmarsh (wetland) in Figure 7C recently have been buried by bodies of white sand that was deposited from storm waves that crashed over the beach and sand dunes. What is the name given to such sand bodies?

13. Photograph 7C was taken from a landform called Aaron's Hill. It is the headland of this part of the island. What will eventually happen to Aaron's Hill? Why?

14. Based upon your answer in Question 13, would Aaron's Hill be a good location for a resort hotel?

15. Based upon your inferences, observations, and explanations in Questions 11, 12, and 13, what will eventually happen to the living saltmarsh in Figures 7B and C?

16. What can you infer about global sea level, based on your answers to Questions 4, 9, and 15?

FIGURE 5: Oceanside, California

North

| 0 | 1 | 2 | 3 kilometers |
| 0 | ½ | 1 | 2 miles |

Contour interval = 25 ft.   1:62,500

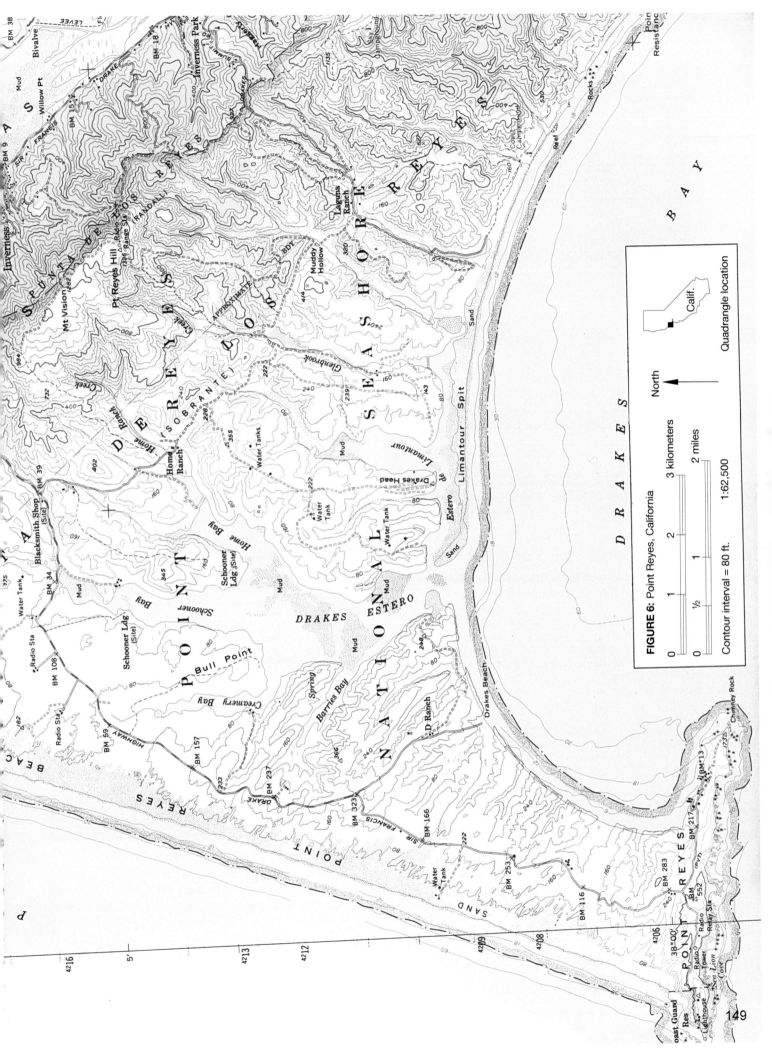

FIGURE 6: Point Reyes, California

North

Quadrangle location

Calif.

| 0 | 1 | 2 | 3 kilometers |

| 0 | ½ | 1 | 2 miles |

Contour interval = 80 ft.   1:62,500

149

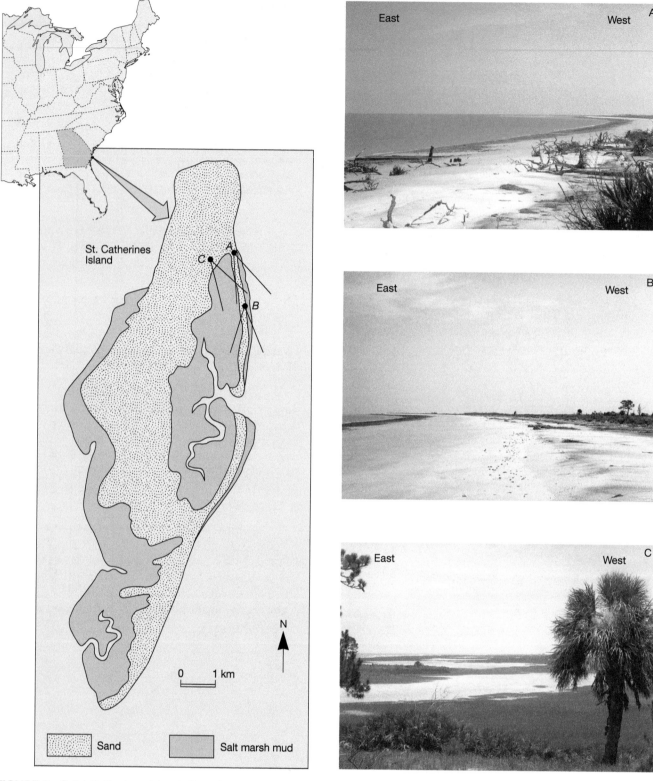

FIGURE 7 Saint Catherines Island, Georgia: coastal features and distribution of sand and saltmarsh mud.
A. View south–southeast from point **A** on map, at low tide. Dark-brown "ribbon" adjacent to ocean is salt-marsh mud. Light-colored area is sand. **B.** View south from point **B** on map at low tide. **C.** View southeast from point **C** (Aaron's Hill) on map. (Photos by R. Busch)

PART B: HUMAN MODIFICATION OF SHORELINES

Examine the portion of the Ocean City, Maryland, topographic quadrangle map provided in Figure 8. Purple features show changes made in 1972 to a 1964 map, so you can see how the coastline changed from 1964–1972. Also note the outline of the barrier island as it appeared in 1849 according to the U.S. Geological Survey.

Ocean City is located on a long, narrow barrier island called Fenwick Island. During a severe hurricane in 1933, the island was breached by tidal currents that formed Ocean City Inlet and split the barrier island in two. Ocean City is still located on what remains of Fenwick Island. The city is a popular vacation resort that has undergone much property development over the past 50 years. The island south of Ocean City Inlet is called Assateague Island. It has remained undeveloped, as a state and national seashore.

Questions

17. After the 1933 hurricane carved out Ocean City Inlet, the Army Corps of Engineers constructed a pair of jetties on each side of the inlet to keep it open. The southern jetty is labeled "seawall" on the map. Sand filled in behind the northern jetty, so it is now a sea wall forming the straight southern edge of Ocean City on Fenwick Island (a straight black line on the map). Based on this information, would you say that the longshore current is traveling north to south, or south to north? Explain.

18. Notice that Assateague Island has migrated landward (west), relative to its 1849 position. This migration began in 1933.

  a. Why did Assateague Island migrate landward?

  b. Field inspection of the west side of Assateague Island reveals that muds of the lagoon (Sinepuxent Bay) are being covered up by the westward-advancing island. What is the rate of Assateague Island's westward migration in feet/year and meters/year?

  c. Based on your last answer (Question 18b), predict the approximate year in which the west side of Assateague Island will merge with saltmarshes around Ocean City Harbor. What natural processes and human activities could prevent this?

19. Notice the groins (short black lines) that have been constructed on the east side of Fenwick Island (Ocean City) in the northeast corner of the map.

  a. Why do you think these groins have been constructed there?

  b. What effect could these groins have on the beaches around Ocean City's Municipal Pier? Why?

20. Hurricanes normally approach Ocean City from the south–southeast. In 1995, one of the largest hurricanes ever recorded (Hurricane Felix) approached Ocean City but miraculously turned back out into the Atlantic Ocean. How does the westward migration of Assateague Island increase the risk of hurricane damage to Ocean City?

21. The westward migration of Assateague Island could be halted and probably reversed if all of the groins, jetties, and sea walls around Ocean City were removed. How would removal of all of these structures place properties in Ocean City at greater risk to environmental damage than they now face?

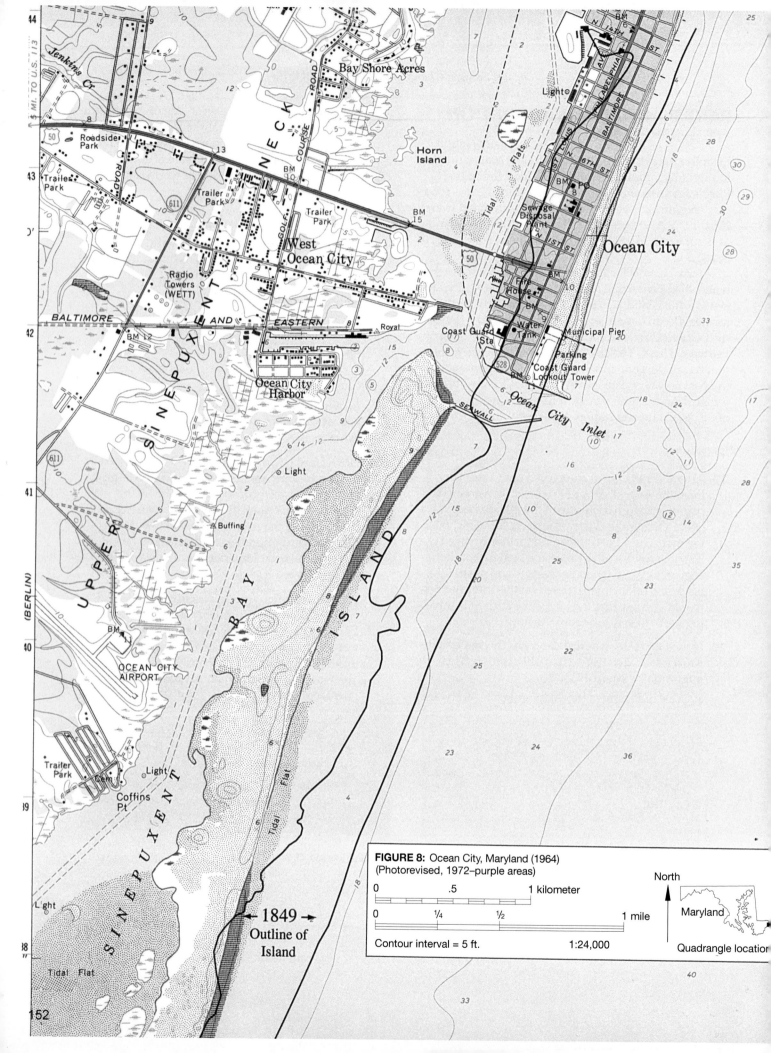

44

Jenkins Cr.

Bay Shore Acres

Horn Island

Ocean City

50

Roadside Park

NECK ROAD

GOLF COURSE ROAD

Light

St. LOUIS AVE

PHILADELPHIA AVE

BALTIMORE AVE

14TH ST

6TH ST

BM

43

Trailer Park

611

Trailer Park

Trailer Park

West Ocean City

BM 15

Tidal Flats

Sewage Disposal Plant

N. 1ST ST

Radio Towers (WETT)

BALTIMORE

SINEPUXENT

AND

EASTERN

Royal

50

Fire House

BM

42

BM 12

Ocean City Harbor

Coast Guard Sta

Water Tank

Municipal Pier

528

Parking

Coast Guard Lookout Tower

ISLAND

NECK

Light

611

Ocean City Inlet

Light

41

Buffing

UPPER

(BERLIN)

BM

40

OCEAN CITY AIRPORT

BAY

SEAWALL

Ocean City

Trailer Park

Cem

Light

Coffins Pt

SINEPUXENT

Tidal Flat

1849 → Outline of Island

Light

FIGURE 8: Ocean City, Maryland (1964)
(Photorevised, 1972–purple areas)

0   .5   1 kilometer

0   1/4   1/2   1 mile

Contour interval = 5 ft.   1:24,000

North

Maryland

Quadrangle location

Tidal Flat

152

PART C: THE THREAT OF RISING SEAS

All of the topographic maps in this laboratory manual rely on a zero reference datum of *mean sea level*. Sea level actually fluctuates both above and below mean sea level during daily tidal cycles and storm surges. A **storm surge** is a bulge of water pushed landward by abnormally high winds and/or low atmospheric pressure associated with storms. Storm surges cause the ocean to rise by about 2–24 feet, depending on the magnitude of the storm. However, except for hurricanes, most storm surges are in the range of 2–3 feet.

Given the fact that daily tides cause sea level to fluctuate 2–3 feet above and below mean sea level, and most storm surges are in the range of 2–3 feet, it might be wise to generally not build dwellings and businesses on elevations less than 6 feet near marine coastlines.

Notice that Ocean City, Maryland (Figure 8) has not followed this rule of thumb. Dense construction (pink areas on Figure 8) has occurred in many areas less than 5 feet above mean sea level. Therefore, Ocean City is at a high risk of flooding from rising sea levels even during normal winter storms. One of these storms flooded most of the city in 1962, and a hurricane could submerge the entire city (because the city's highest elevation is only 10 feet above mean sea level).

A more long-term hazard to coastal cities is the threat that mean sea level may rise significantly over the coming decades. A report on *The Probability of Sea Level Rise* was issued by the U.S. Environmental Protection Agency (EPA) in 1996, and was based on data from dozens of the most respected researchers in this field throughout the world. The report demonstrates that mean sea level is already rising at rates of 2.5–3.0 mm/yr (10–12 inches per century) along U.S. coastlines, and these rates are expected to increase. According to this comprehensive study, there is a 50% probability that sea level will rise 34 cm (about 13 inches) over the next century. A 50% probability is the same probability that you will get heads if you flip a coin. The EPA study also suggests that there is only a 1% probability (1 chance in 100) that sea level will rise 104 cm (well over 3 feet) over the next century.

In planning for safe and economical coastal development, planning commissions and real estate developers could "play it safe" and assume that sea level could rise about 1 meter (about 3 feet) in the next century.

Questions

22. From our discussion on storm surges and the threat of actual sea-level rise, it seems logical that there are two main rules of planning for safe and economical coastal development in relation to the threat of property damage from coastal flooding. Planners should account for the probability that storm surges will normally cause sea level to rise approximately 6 feet above mean sea level. Planners should also account for the long-term probability that mean sea level will actually rise approximately 3 feet over the next century. Given the fact that most existing topographic maps of coastal areas have contour intervals of 5 feet, what would you suggest as the contour line below which construction should not occur along coastlines? Explain.

23. Let us assume that dwellings constructed at elevations less than 10 feet above mean sea level are at increasingly high risk to flooding over the next century. Using a blue colored pencil, color in all of the land areas in Figure 9 (Charleston, South Carolina) that are now at elevations less than and equal to 10 feet above mean sea level.

    a. What amount of the new buildings (purple buildings in Figure 9) in Charleston have been built in this high-risk, 10-foot zone?

    b. Why do you think that so much new construction has occurred in the high-risk, 10-foot zone around Charleston?

    c. What effect would a 10-foot sea level rise have on the abundant saltmarshes (wetlands) in the Charleston region?

24. Study the map of Miami, Florida (Figure 10), and list some of the significant properties that are now located within the high-risk, 10-foot zone where flood hazards will increase over the next century.

FIGURE 9: Charleston, South Carolina (1979)

Contour interval = 5 ft.   1:24,000

North

South Carolina

Quadrangle location

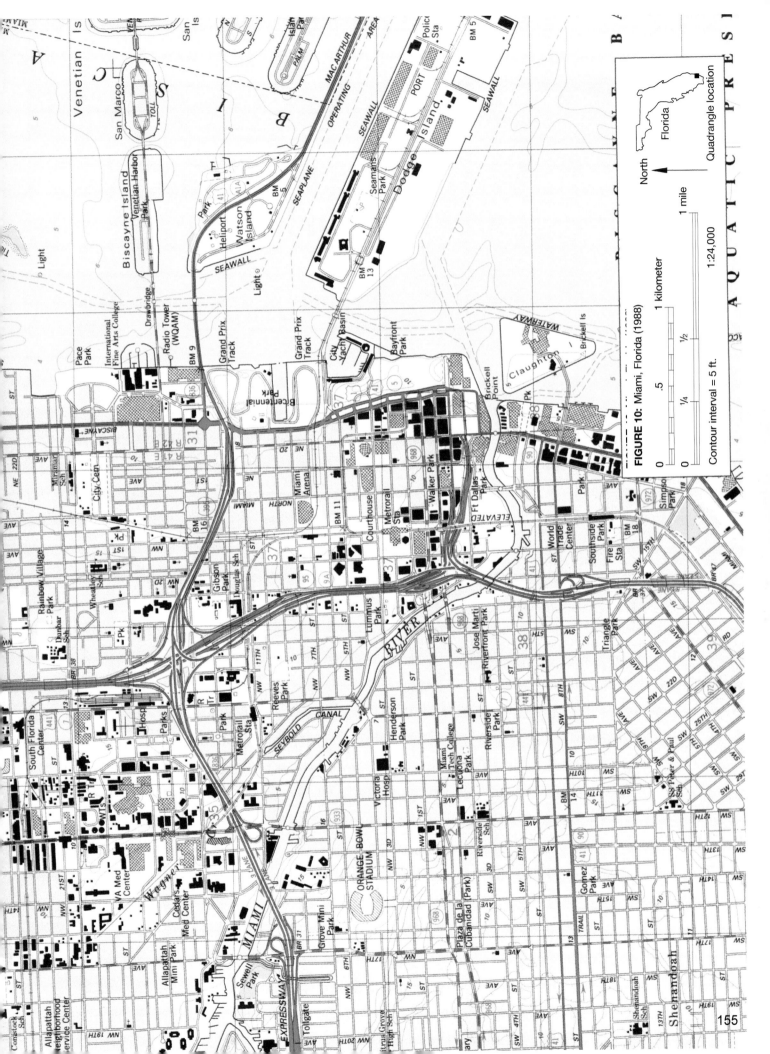

FIGURE 10: Miami, Florida (1988)

Contour interval = 5 ft.

Quadrangle location

Florida

North

| | 1 kilometer |
| 0 | .5 | |

| | 1 mile |
| 0 | 1/4 | 1/2 | |

1:24,000

155

Earthquake Hazards and Human Risks

•CONTRIBUTING AUTHORS•

Thomas H. Anderson • *University of Pittsburgh*

David N. Lumsden • *University of Memphis*

Pamela J.W. Gore • *Georgia Perimeter College*

OBJECTIVES

A. Experiment with models to determine how earthquake damage to buildings is related to the Earth materials on which they are constructed. Apply your experimental results to evaluate earthquake hazards and human risks in San Francisco.

B. Graph seismic data to construct and evaluate travel time curves for P-waves, S-waves, and L-waves. Use seismograms and your travel time curves to locate the epicenter of an earthquake.

C. Analyze and evaluate active faults using remote sensing and geologic maps.

D. Interpret seismograms to infer relative movements along the New Madrid Fault System within the North American Plate.

E. Explore real-time earthquake data, hazards, and impacts on humans using resources from the Internet.

MATERIALS

Pencil, eraser, laboratory notebook, ruler, calculator, drafting compass, several coins, a small plastic or paper cup containing dry sediment (fine sand, sugar, or salt), and a wash bottle.

INTRODUCTION

Earthquakes are shaking motions and vibrations of the Earth caused by large releases of energy that accompany volcanic eruptions, explosions, and movements of Earth's bedrock along fault lines. News reports usually describe an earthquake's **epicenter,** which is the point on Earth's surface (location on a map) directly above the **focus** (underground origin of the earthquake, in bedrock). The episodic releases of energy that occur along fault lines strain the bedrock like a person jumping on a diving board. This strain produces elastic waves of vibration and shaking called **seismic waves** (earthquake waves). Seismic waves originate at the earthquake's focus and travel in all directions through the rock body of Earth and along Earth's surface. The surface seismic waves travel in all directions from the epicenter, like the rings of ripples (small waves) that form when a stone is cast into a pond. In fact, people who have experienced strong surface seismic waves report that they saw and felt wave after wave of elastic motion passing by like the above-mentioned ripples on a pond. These waves are strongest near the epicenter and grow weaker with distance from the epicenter. For example, when a strong earthquake struck Mexico City in 1985, it caused massive property damage and 9500 deaths in a circular area radiating about 400 km (250 mi) in every direction from the city. By the time these same surface seismic waves of energy had traveled 3200 km to Pennsylvania, they were so weak that people could not even feel them passing beneath their feet. They did, however, cause water levels in wells and swimming pools to fluctuate by as much as 12 cm. They also were recorded by earthquake-detecting instruments called *seismographs*. Therefore, although most damage from an earthquake usually occurs close to its epicenter, seismographs can detect the

From *Laboratory Manual in Physical Geology*, Eighth Edition, American Geological Institute, National Association of Geoscience Teachers, Richard M. Busch, Dennis Tasa. Copyright © 2009 by American Geological Institute. Published by Pearson Prentice Hall. All rights reserved.

earthquake's waves of energy even when they travel through Earth's rocky body or along Earth's surface to locations thousands of kilometers away from the epicenter.

Fault motions (movements of Earth's crust along breaks in the rocks) are the most common source of earthquakes felt by people. These motions can occur along faults that do not break the Earth's surface or along faults that do break the Earth's surface. Fault motions at Earth's surface can directly cause *hazards* such as the destruction of buildings, breakage of pipes and electric lines, development of open fissures in the soil, change in the course of streams, and generation of tsunamis (destructive ocean waves, generally 1–10 m high, that devastate coastal environments). However, *all* earthquakes cause some degree of vibration and shaking of the Earth, which can also cause most of the above-mentioned hazards.

Therefore people who live where strong earthquakes occur are at *risk* for experiencing personal injury, property damage, and disruption of their livelihoods and daily routines. Geologists study seismic waves, map active faults, determine the nature of earthquake-induced hazards, assess human risk where such hazards occur, and assist in the development of government policies related to public safety in earthquake-prone regions.

PART A: SIMULATE EARTHQUAKE HAZARDS TO ESTIMATE RISKS

Geoscientists and engineers commonly simulate earthquakes in the laboratory to observe their effects on models of construction sites, buildings, bridges, and so on. Now is your turn to give it a try. Start by making simple models of buildings constructed in dry, uncompacted sediment (Model 1) and moist, compacted sediment (Model 2). Then simulate earthquakes and observe what happens to them.

Questions

Obtain a small plastic or paper cup. Fill it three-quarters full with a dry sediment like sand, dirt, salt, or sugar. Place several coins in the sediment so they resemble vertical walls of buildings constructed on a substrate of uncompacted sediment (as in Figure 1). This is Model 1. Observe what happens to Model 1 when you *simulate an earthquake* by tapping the cup on a table top while you also rotate it counterclockwise.

1. What happened to the vertically positioned coins in the uncompacted sediment of Model 1 when you simulated an earthquake?

FIGURE 1 Photograph of Model 1 being subjected to a simulated earthquake.

Now make Model 2. Remove the coins from Model 1, and add a small bit of water to the sediment in the cup so that it is moist (but not soupy). Press down on the sediment in the cup so that it is well compacted, and then place the coins into this compacted sediment just as you placed them in Model 1 earlier. *Simulate an earthquake* as you did for Model 1, and then answer Questions 2 and 3.

2. What happened to the vertically positioned coins in the compacted sediment of Model 2 when you simulated an earthquake?

3. Based on your experimental Models 1 and 2, which kind of Earth material is more hazardous to build on in earthquake-prone regions: compacted sediment or uncompacted sediment? (Justify your answer by citing evidence from your experimental models.)

4. Consider the moist, compacted sediment in Model 2. Do you think this material would become *more* hazardous to build on, or *less* hazardous to build on, if it became totally saturated with water during a rainy season? (To find out and justify your answer, design and conduct another experimental model of your own. Call it Model 3.)

5. Write a statement that summarizes how water in a sandy substrate beneath a home can be beneficial or hazardous. Justify your reasoning with reference to your experimental models.

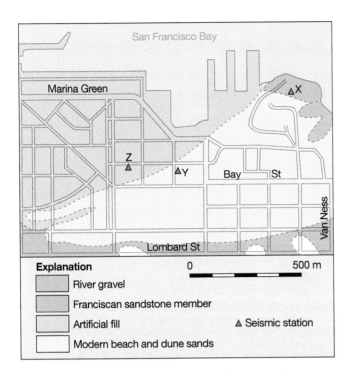

FIGURE 2 Map of the nature and distribution of Earth materials on which buildings and roads have been constructed for a portion of San Francisco, California. (Courtesy of U.S. Geological Survey)

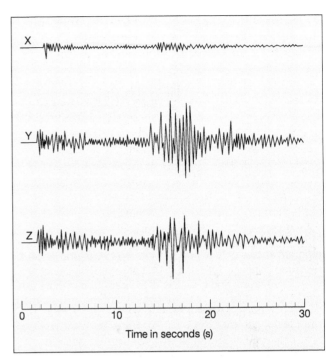

FIGURE 3 Seismograms recorded at Stations **X**, **Y**, and **Z**, for a strong (Richter Magnitude 4.6) aftershock of the Loma Prieta, California, earthquake. During the earthquake, little damage occurred at **X**, but significant damage to houses occurred at **Y** and **Z**. (Courtesy of U.S. Geological Survey)

San Francisco is located in a tectonically active region, so it occasionally experiences strong earthquakes. Figure 2 is a map showing the kinds of Earth materials upon which buildings have been constructed in a portion of San Francisco. These materials include hard compact Franciscan Sandstone, uncompacted beach and dune sands, river gravel, and artificial fill. The artificial fill is mostly debris from buildings destroyed in the great 1906 earthquake that reduced large portions of the city to blocks of rubble. Also note that three locations have been labeled **X**, **Y**, and **Z** on Figure 2. Imagine that you have been hired by an insurance company to assess what risk there may be in buying newly constructed apartment buildings located at **X**, **Y**, and **Z** on Figure 2. Your job is to infer whether the risk of property damage during strong earthquakes is **low** (little or no damage expected) or **high** (damage can be expected). All that you have as a basis for reasoning is Figure 2 and knowledge of your experiments with models in Questions 1–4.

6. What is the risk at location **X**? Why?

7. What is the risk at location **Y**? Why?

8. What is the risk at location **Z**? Why?

On October 17, 1989, just as Game 3 of the World Series was about to start in San Francisco, a strong earthquake occurred at Loma Prieta, California, and shook the entire San Francisco Bay area. Seismographs at locations **X**, **Y**, and **Z** (see Figure 2) recorded the shaking, and the resulting seismograms are shown in Figure 3. Earthquakes are recorded on the seismograms as deviations (vertical zigzags) from a flat, horizontal line. Thus, notice that much more shaking occurred at locations **Y** and **Z** than at location **X**.

9. The Loma Prieta earthquake caused no significant damage at location **X**, but there was moderate damage to buildings at location **Y** and severe damage at location **Z**. Explain how this damage report compares to your predictions of risk in Questions 6, 7, and 8.

10. The Loma Prieta earthquake shook all of the San Francisco Bay region. Yet Figure 3 is evidence that the earthquake had very different effects on properties located only 600 m apart. Explain how the kind of substrate (uncompacted vs. firm and compacted) on which buildings are constructed influences how much the buildings are shaken and damaged in an earthquake.

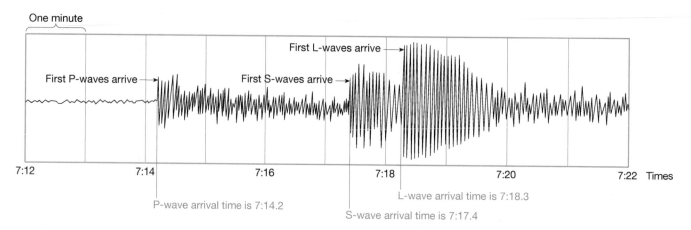

FIGURE 4 Seismogram of a New Guinea earthquake recorded at a location in Australia. Most of the seismogram shows only minor background deviations (short zigzags) from a horizontal line, such as the interval recorded between 7:12 and 7:14. Large vertical deviations indicate motions caused by the arrival of P-waves, S-waves, and L-waves of the earthquake (note arrows with labels). By making detailed measurements with a ruler, you can determine that the arrival time of the P-waves was 7:14.2 (14.2 minutes past 7 o'clock), the arrival time of the S-waves was 7:17.4, and the arrival time of the L-waves was 7:18.3.

11. Imagine that you are a member of the San Francisco City Council. What actions could you propose to **mitigate** (decrease the probability of) future earthquake hazards such as the damage that occurred at locations **Y** and **Z** in the Loma Prieta earthquake?

PART B: GRAPHING SEISMIC DATA AND LOCATING THE EPICENTER OF AN EARTHQUAKE

An earthquake produces three main types of seismic waves that radiate from its focus/epicenter at different rates. Seismographs are instruments used to detect these seismic waves and produce a **seismogram**—a record of seismic wave motions obtained at a specific recording station (Figure 4).

Seismograms can detect and record several types of *body waves*, which are seismic waves that travel through Earth's interior (rather than along its surface) and radiate in all directions from the focus. Two of these body waves are used to locate earthquake epicenters:

- **P-waves:** *P* for primary, because they travel fastest and arrive at seismographs first. (They are compressional, or "push-pull" waves.)

- **S-waves:** *S* for secondary, because they travel more slowly and arrive at seismographs after the P-waves. (They are perpendicular, shear, or "side-to-side" waves.)

Seismographs also detect the surface seismic waves, called **L-waves** or *Love waves* (named for A. E. H. Love, who discovered them). L-waves travel along Earth's surface (a longer route than the body waves) and thus are recorded after the S-waves and P-waves arrive at the seismograph.

Figure 4 is a seismogram recorded at a station located in Australia. Seismic waves arrived there from an earthquake epicenter located 1800 kilometers (1125 miles) away in New Guinea. Notice that the seismic waves were recorded as deviations (vertical zigzags) from the nearly horizontal line of normal background vibrations. Thus, the first pulse of seismic waves was P-waves, which had an **arrival time** of 7:14.2 (i.e., 14.2 minutes after 7:00). The second pulse of seismic waves was the slower S-waves, which had an arrival time of 7:17.4. The final pulse of seismic waves was the L-waves that traveled along Earth's surface, so they did not begin to arrive until 7:18.3. The earthquake actually occurred at the New Guinea epicenter at 7:10:23 (10 minutes and 23 seconds after 7:00) Greenwich Mean Time, which can be written as 7:10.4. Therefore the **travel time of the main seismic waves** (to go 1800 km) was 3.8 minutes for P-waves (7:14.2 minus 7:10.4), 7.0 minutes for S-waves (7:17.4 minus 7:10.4), and 7.9 minutes for L-waves (7:18.3 minus 7:10.4).

Notice the seismic data provided in Figure 5 for 11 recording stations where seismograms were recorded after the same New Guinea earthquake (at 3° North latitude and 140° East longitude). The **distance from epicenter** (surface distance between the recording station and the epicenter) and travel time of main seismic waves are provided for each

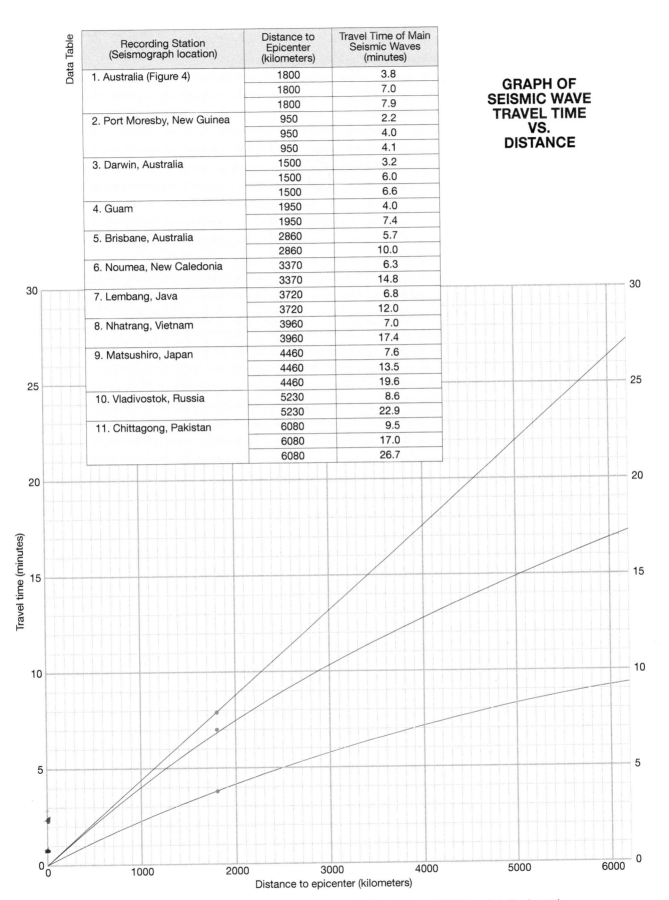

Data Table	Recording Station (Seismograph location)	Distance to Epicenter (kilometers)	Travel Time of Main Seismic Waves (minutes)
	1. Australia (Figure 4)	1800	3.8
		1800	7.0
		1800	7.9
	2. Port Moresby, New Guinea	950	2.2
		950	4.0
		950	4.1
	3. Darwin, Australia	1500	3.2
		1500	6.0
		1500	6.6
	4. Guam	1950	4.0
		1950	7.4
	5. Brisbane, Australia	2860	5.7
		2860	10.0
	6. Noumea, New Caledonia	3370	6.3
		3370	14.8
	7. Lembang, Java	3720	6.8
		3720	12.0
	8. Nhatrang, Vietnam	3960	7.0
		3960	17.4
	9. Matsushiro, Japan	4460	7.6
		4460	13.5
		4460	19.6
	10. Vladivostok, Russia	5230	8.6
		5230	22.9
	11. Chittagong, Pakistan	6080	9.5
		6080	17.0
		6080	26.7

GRAPH OF SEISMIC WAVE TRAVEL TIME VS. DISTANCE

FIGURE 5   Seismic wave data for an earthquake that occurred in New Guinea (at 3° North latitude and 140° East longitude) at Greenwich Mean Time of 7 hours, 10 minutes, 23 seconds (7:10.4). The travel time of a main seismic wave is the time interval between when the earthquake occurred in New Guinea and when that wave first arrived at a recording location. The surface distance is the distance between the recording location and the earthquake epicenter. Graph is for plotting points that represent the travel time of each main seismic wave at each location versus the surface distance that it traveled.

recording station. Notice that the data from most of the recording stations includes travel times for all three main kinds of seismic waves (P-waves, S-waves, and L-waves). However, instruments at some locations recorded only one or two kinds of waves. Location 1 is the Australian recording station where the seismogram in Figure 4 was obtained.

Questions

12. On the graph paper provided at the base of Figure 5, *plot points in pencil to show the travel time of each main seismic wave in relation to its distance from the epicenter* (when recorded on the seismogram at the recording station). For example, the data for location 1 (obtained from Figure 4) have already been plotted as red points on Figure 5. Recording station 1 was located 1800 km from the earthquake epicenter and the main waves had travel times of 3.8 minutes, 7.0 minutes, and 7.9 minutes. Plot points in pencil for data from all of the remaining recording stations, and then examine the graph.

Notice that your points do not produce a *random pattern*. They fall in *discrete paths* close to the three narrow black lines (or curves) already drawn on the graph. These black lines (or curves) were formed by plotting many thousands of points from hundreds of earthquakes, exactly as you just plotted your points. Explain why you think that your points, and all of the points from other earthquakes, occur along three discrete lines (or curves).

13. Study the three discrete, narrow black lines (or curves) of points in Figure 5. Label the line (curve) of points that represents travel times of the P-waves. Label the line or curve that connects the points representing travel times of the S-waves. Label the line or curve that connects the points representing travel times of the L-waves. Why is the S-wave curve steeper than the P-wave curve?

14. Why do the L-wave data points form a straight line whereas data points for P-waves and S-waves form curves? (*Hint:* The curved lines are evidence of how the physical environments and rocks deep inside Earth are different from the physical environments and rocks just beneath Earth's surface.)

15. Notice that the origin on your graph (travel time of zero and distance of zero) represents the location of the earthquake epicenter and the start of the seismic waves. The time interval between first

arrival of P-waves and first arrival of S-waves at the same recording station is called the **S-minus-P time interval**. How does the S-minus-P time interval change with distance from the epicenter?

16. Imagine that an earthquake occurred this morning. The first P-waves of the earthquake were recorded at a recording station in Houston at 6:12.6 a.m. and the first S-waves arrived at the same Houston station at 6:17.1 a.m. Use Figure 5 to determine an answer for each question below.

a. What is the S-minus-P time interval of the earthquake?

b. How far from the earthquake's epicenter is the Houston recording station located?

c. You have determined the distance (radius of a circle on a map) between Houston and the earthquake epicenter. What additional data would you require to determine the location of the earthquake's epicenter (point on a map), and how would you use the data to locate the epicenter?

Locate the Epicenter of an Earthquake

See if you can use the travel time curves in Figure 5 to locate the epicenter (point on a map) of the earthquake that produced the seismograms in Figure 6. These seismograms were recorded at stations in Alaska, North Carolina, and Hawaii.

Questions

17. Estimate, to the nearest tenth of a minute, the times that P-waves and S-waves first arrived at each recording station (seismograph location) in Figure 6. Then, subtract P from S to get the S-minus-P time interval:

	First P arrival	First S arrival	S-minus-P
Sitka, AK	_____	_____	_____
Charlotte, NC	_____	_____	_____
Honolulu, HI	_____	_____	_____

18. Using the S-minus-P time intervals and Figure 5, determine the distance from epicenter (in kilometers) for each recording station.

Sitka, AK _____ kilometers

Charlotte, NC _____ kilometers

Honolulu, HI _____ kilometers

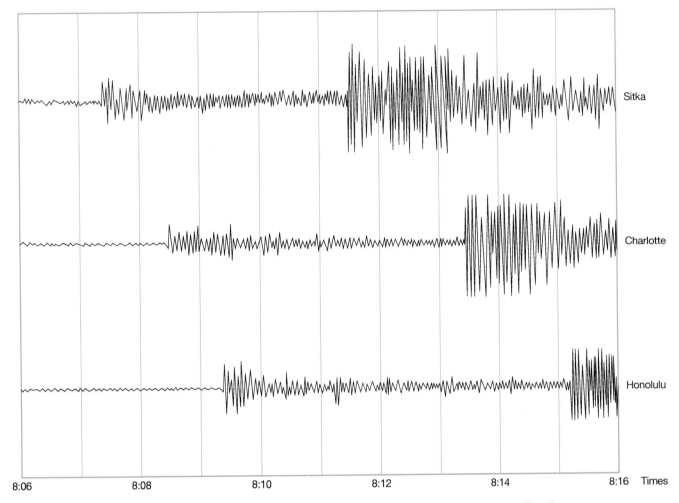

FIGURE 6 Seismograms for an earthquake recorded at three different locations in Alaska, North Carolina, and Hawaii. Times have been standardized to Charlotte, North Carolina, to simplify comparison.

19. Next, find the earthquake's epicenter using the distances just obtained.

a. First use the geographic coordinates below to locate and mark the three recording stations on the world map in Figure 7.

Sitka, AK: 57°N latitude, 135°W longitude

Charlotte, NC: 35°N latitude, 81°W longitude

Honolulu, HI: 21°N latitude, 158°W longitude

b. Use a drafting compass to draw a circle around each recording station. Make the radius of each circle equal to the *distance from epicenter* determined for the station in Question 18. (Use the scale on Figure 7 to set this radius on your drafting compass.) The circles you draw should intersect approximately at one point on the map. This point is the epicenter. (If the three circles do not quite intersect at a single point, then find a point that is equidistant from the three edges of the circles, and use this as the epicenter.) Record the location of the earthquake epicenter:

N Latitude _____ W Longitude _____

20. What is the name of a major fault that occurs near this epicenter?

163

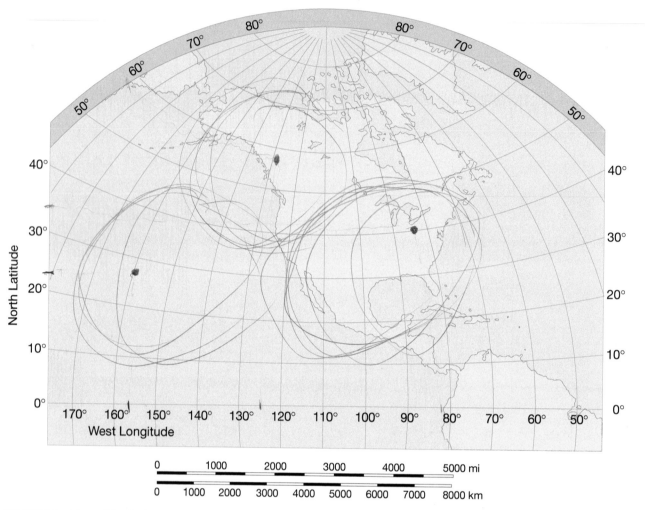

FIGURE 7 Map of Earth, for use in plotting data and locating the earthquake's epicenter.

PART C: ANALYSIS OF ACTIVE FAULTS USING AERIAL PHOTOGRAPHS

There are many faults that can be imaged, photographed, mapped, and studied where they break Earth's surface. Some of these faults are **active faults,** meaning that they can move and generate earthquakes at the present time.

Examine the aerial photograph of a portion of southern California (Figure 8) for evidence of faults and fault motions. Notice the roads, small streams, and fine features of the landscape. Also notice that the figure shows a portion of the San Andreas Fault, which is a tectonic plate boundary separating the Pacific Plate from the North American Plate.

Questions

21. Geologists have inferred that the San Andreas Fault is an active fault and that the blocks of rock on either side of the fault are moving in the directions indicated with half-arrows.

   a. What evidence, visible in this photograph, could you use to suggest that this fault is both active and moving relative to the arrows? Explain your reasoning.

   b. How much has the San Andreas Fault offset the present-day channel of Wallace Creek?

   c. Is the San Andreas Fault a left-lateral fault or a right-lateral fault? Explain.

22. How wide is the San Andreas Fault (tectonic plate boundary) here?

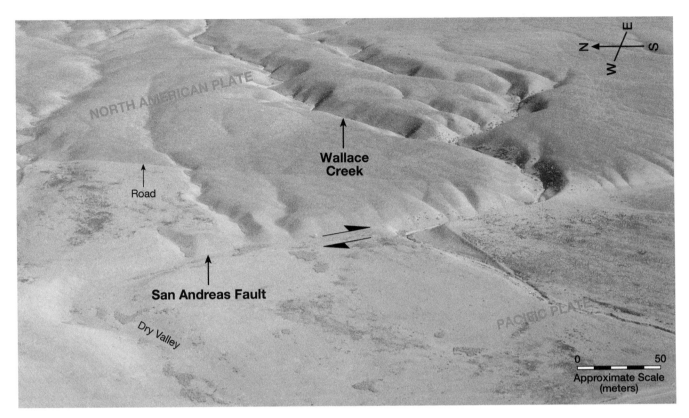

FIGURE 8   Aerial photograph of a portion of the San Andreas Fault (a tectonic plate boundary) at Wallace Creek, Carrizo Plain, southern California. (Photo by Randall Marrett, University of Texas, Austin)

23. Notice the small dry valley in the lower-left part of the photograph. Infer how this valley may have formed.

PART D: DETERMINING RELATIVE MOTIONS ALONG THE NEW MADRID FAULT ZONE

The relative motions of blocks of rock on either side of a fault zone can be determined by mapping the way the pen on a seismograph moved (up or down on the seismogram) when P-waves first arrived at various seismic stations adjacent to the fault. This pen motion is called **first motion** and represents the reaction of the P-wave to dilation (pulling rocks apart) or compression (squeezing rocks together) as observed on seismograms (see Figure 9, left).

If the first movement of the P-wave was up on a seismogram, then that recording station (where the seismogram was obtained) experienced compression during the earthquake. If the first movement of the P-wave was down on a seismogram, then that recording station was dilational during the earthquake. What

was the first motion at all of the seismic stations in Figure 3? (Answer: The first movement of the pen was up for each P-wave, so the first motion at all three sites was compressional.)

By plotting the first motions observed at recording stations on both sides of a fault that has experienced an earthquake, a picture of the relative motions of the fault emerges. For example, notice that the first motions observed at seismic stations on either side of a hypothetical fault are plotted in relation to the fault in Figure 9 (right side). The half-arrows indicate how motion proceeded away from seismic stations where dilation was recorded and toward seismic stations where compression was recorded (for each side of the fault). So the picture of relative motion along this fault is that Block **X** is moving southeast and Block **Y** is moving northwest. Now study a real example using Figures 10 and 11.

The New Madrid Fault System is located within the *Mississippi Embayment*, a basin filled with Mesozoic and Cenozoic rocks that rest unconformably on (and are surrounded by) Paleozoic and Precambrian rocks (see Figure 11). Faults of the New Madrid System are not visible on satellite images and photographs, because

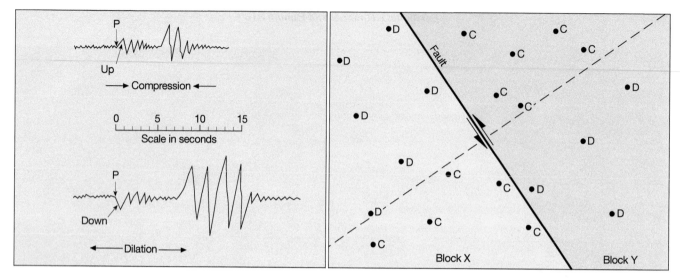

FIGURE 9 **Left**—Sketch of typical seismograms for compressional first motion (first P-wave motion is up) compared with dilational first motion (first P-wave motion is down). **Right**—Map of a hypothetical region showing a fault along which an earthquake has occurred, and the P-wave first motions (C = compressional, D = dilational) observed for the earthquake at seismic stations adjacent to the fault. Stress moves away from the field of dilation and toward the field of compression on each side of the fault (large open arrows), so the relative motion of the fault is as indicated by the smaller half-arrows.

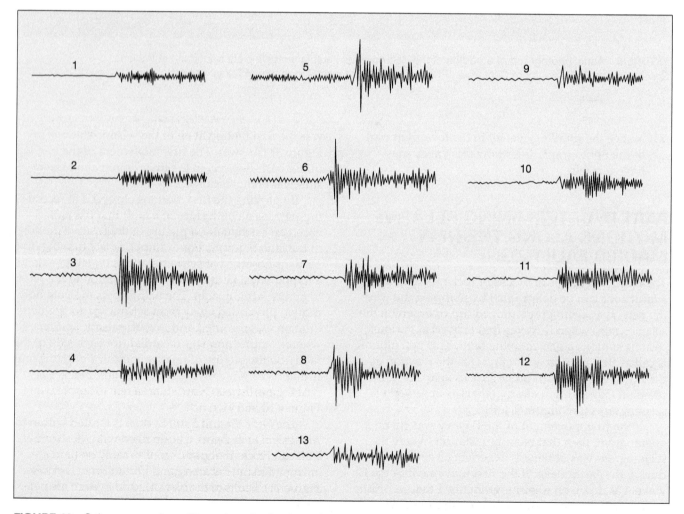

FIGURE 10 Seismograms from 13 numbered seismic stations in the Mississippi Embayment after an earthquake that occurred in the New Madrid Fault System. Numbers in this figure correspond to the numbered sites on the map in Figure 11.

166

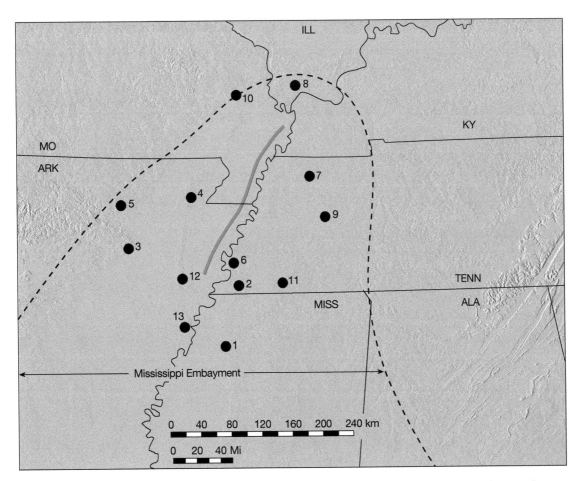

FIGURE 11 Map of a portion of the Mississippi Embayment showing the generalized surface geology, location (in red) of the main fault of the New Madrid (Blind) Fault System, numbered seismic stations (as in Figure 10), and state boundaries.

they are **blind faults** (faults that do not break Earth's surface). These blind faults occur in the Paleozoic and Precambrian rocks that are buried beneath approximately a kilometer of Mesozoic and Cenozoic rocks.

The main fault of the New Madrid System is plotted in red on Figure 11. It is well known, because a series of strong earthquakes occurred along it in 1811 and 1812. One of these earthquakes was the strongest earthquake ever recorded in North America, and the potential for more strong earthquakes here is a lingering hazard. The locations of 13 seismic stations are also plotted on Figure 11. Seismograms obtained at these stations (after an earthquake along the New Madrid Fault System) are provided in Figure 10.

Question

24. Analyze the seismograms in Figure 10 to determine if their P-wave first motions indicate compression or dilation (refer to Figure 9 as needed). Plot this information on Figure 11 by writing a *C* beside the stations where compression occurred and a *D* beside the stations where dilation occurred. When you have finished plotting these letters, draw half-arrows on Figure 11 to indicate the relative motions of the blocks of rock on either side of the main fault. Does the main fault have a right-lateral motion or a left-lateral motion? Explain.

Unlike most major active fault zones that occur at plate boundaries (such as the San Andreas Fault), the New Madrid Fault System is an active and hazardous system of faults that occurs *within* the North American Plate. Intraplate stresses are apparently causing adjustments along these blind faults and the potential for more earthquakes that place humans at risk.

PART E: TRACKING EARTHQUAKE HAZARDS IN REAL TIME AND ASSESSING THEIR IMPACT ON RISK TAKERS

Find and explore Internet sites that contain real-time information about earthquake hazards and risks (go to **http://www.prenhall.com/agi**). Record the date and time that you conducted this exploration, and proceed to the items below.

Questions

25. How many earthquakes of Richter Magnitude 2.5 or greater have occurred in each of the following areas in the past week?

a. Southern California (from motions along a plate boundary):

b. Hawaii (from tectonism at the world's most active hot spot):

c. Along the New Madrid Fault Zone (from intraplate stresses):

26. From your answers in Question 25, which plate tectonic setting seems to generate:

a. the most earthquakes? Why?

b. the fewest earthquakes? Why?

27. Search the Federal Emergency Management Agency server (**http://www.fema.gov/**) to find out about some of the damage done to properties and lives of people after a strong earthquake. What should *you* do:

a. to *prepare* for a strong earthquake?

b. to *survive during and shortly after* a strong earthquake?

Index

172